TO: JACK STOVER

I ENCOURAGE YOU TO TRANSFORM
YOUR INNER MOST MARKETABLE
PASSIONS INTO YOUR PROFESSION.
DREAM, PLAN, EXECUTE & SOAR!

Patrick Snow

What Others Are Saying
about Patrick Snow
and This Book

"More Americans put families ahead of work. Family is important to Patrick Snow. He is a speaker, coach and author of *Creating Your Own Destiny*. Employees used to be willing to sacrifice because of things like stock options. Now they are fed up. They realize that family is the only stabilizing force in today's turbulent economy. Making time for family isn't just important for a few employees like Snow—it's a growing priority for many workers disillusioned by layoffs, corporate scandal, and waning corporate loyalty. Seventy percent of employees don't think there is a healthy balance between work and personal life."

USA TODAY
Cover Story, December 5, 2002

"When Patrick Snow decided to leave his corporate sales job, he called three friends to solicit advice. 'The employee handbook was good for a general overview, but it failed to answer some of my specific questions,' said Mr. Snow, who left to start his own professional speaking business. 'Lucky for me, the information my buddies gave me enabled me to plan my exit strategy.'"

The New York Times
September 4, 2005

"Patrick Snow dedicated five years of his life and invested $20,000 to publish his first book, *Creating Your Own Destiny*. Immediately thereafter, he started being invited to keynote conferences to share his experiences and to serve as a coach helping other entrepreneurs publish their own books."

Forbes
November 2012

"During early mornings, evenings and weekends in his 10 years in corporate sales, Patrick Snow built up a side business of coaching, speaking and consulting. Eventually, he quit his job to pursue his passion full-time. A decade later, Snow now travels the world as a professional speaker and coaches others in entrepreneurship and small-business ownership."

Midweek Oahu
April 9, 2014

"Small-business consultant Patrick Snow is frequently asked for the best way to attract more paying clients. His answer: Write and publish your book and give it away to prospects. This works, he says because it allows you to stand out from the crowd, boost your credentials and give you more credibility."

Hawaii Business
May 2014

"If you want to develop the mindset of a world champion, then start young by reading this book and applying its wisdom to your life, your business, and your family!"

— Egan Inoue
Author of *Becoming Relentless*
11-Time World-Champion Athlete and
Founder of Hawaii Fit Camp

"This amazing little book will transform you from mediocrity to astounding success in a short time frame. This book is brilliantly written and you will be forever impacted by its message!"

— Kieran Murry
Author of *Go for Your Gold* and
co-founder of Ignite-U

"This book is for anyone with a son and / or daughter who wants him / her to a get a jumpstart on life."

— Randall Broad
Author of *It's an Extraordinary Life*

"Once again, Patrick Snow delivers awe-inspiring content mirroring the success he has achieved personally and which he strives to instill in the lives of his readers, globally. His storytelling style is a true motivator that begins on page one of this book."

— Heather Allen
Author of *Let Your Creativity Work for You*

"Patrick Snow has done it again! This book is sure to guide you to want to create your own destiny!"

— Seconde Nimenya
Author of *Evolving Through Adversity*

"Join Patrick Snow, the best-selling author of *Creating Your Own Destiny,* as he takes you on the creative, classic, personal journey of a humble boy who becomes a successful entrepreneur."

— Jim R. Jacobs
Author of *Driving Lessons for Life*

"Where was this book when I was twelve and selling candy bars door-to-door? If I had read *Boy Entrepreneur* back then, I'd be leap years ahead in operating my own business now. I can't wait to see what the next generation will do with the priceless knowledge in this book!"

— Tyler R. Tichelaar, Ph.D.
Author of *Arthur's Legacy*, and owner of
Superior Book Productions

"Finally, a book that teaches free enterprise to today's youth. Young or old, man or woman, boy or girl, this resource is exactly what every entrepreneur needs in his or her marketing toolbox."

— Lori Chaffin
Publisher of *Hawaii Wellness Directory*

"Destined to become a classic, Patrick Snow's book *Boy Entrepreneur* inspires both young and old to embrace the concepts of building and creating their own destinies."

— Eric J. Scroggins, Ph.D.
Author of *Vision Blockers*

"This is a great story of true grit, raw determination, and sheer perseverance! You will love each and every lesson from some of the world's most successful entrepreneurs."

— Wanek Stein
Author of *The Swiss Perspective*

"Have you ever wondered what the missing success link is for achieving your destiny? You'll find it in this book!"

— Dr. Taylor Clark
Author of *Beating All Odds*

"This book is a game-changer for anyone who wants to succeed in business. There are many books out there that give advice, but Patrick Snow has taken the next step to inspire you through stories that are easy to understand yet sophisticated enough to challenge your mind."

— David S. Chang
Author of *The Art of Thinking Smart*
CEO of Chang Holding Company

"Because it's never too early for kids to learn entrepreneurial principles, this motivating and empowering book guides you effortlessly through the steps needed to succeed in business."

— Susan Friedmann
International Best-Selling Author of
Riches in Niches

"This little gem optimizes the quote that big things come in small packages. Don't let the size fool you. A dime is half the size of a nickel, but it's worth twice as much. With this book, be prepared to reap much more than you sow!"

— Kevin Hocker
Award-Winning Author of *The Success Compass*

"Fun, inspiring, and motivational! You will never look at your business the same."

— Mark Porteous
Author of *Maximizing Your Human Experience*

"Parents everywhere on the planet need to share this book with their children if they want them to become successful, confident, and happy adults. Adults everywhere need to apply the 50 Greatest Sales & Marketing Secrets to their businesses if they want to succeed."

— Nicole Gabriel
Author of *Finding Your Inner Truth*

"The jump is so frightening
between where I am,
and where I want to be...
because of all I may become,
I will close my eyes and leap!"

– Mary Anne Radmacher

BOY
ENTREPRENEUR

HOW ONE HAWAI`I KID
SUCEEDED IN BUSINES
(AND YOU CAN TOO)

PATRICK SNOW

AVIVA
PUBLISHING
New York

BOY ENTREPRENEUR
How One Hawai`i Kid Succeeded in Business (And You Can Too)

Published by:
Aviva Publishing
Lake Placid, NY
(518) 523-1320
www.AvivaPubs.com

Patrick Snow
Telephone: 206-310-1200
Email: Patrick@PatrickSnow.com
www.BoyEntrepreneur.com
www.PatrickSnow.com

ISBN: 978-1-940984-37-7

Library of Congress: 2014942236

Editor: Tyler Tichelaar
Cover Designer: Nicole Gabriel / Angel Dog Productions
Interior Book Layout: Nicole Gabriel / Angel Dog Productions
Author Photo: Janet Becker

Every attempt has been made to properly source all quotes.

Printed in the United States of America

First Edition

2 4 6 8 10 12

DEDICATION

To my fiancée, Nicole: You are the most incredible person to come into my life. I love you deeply with all my heart and soul. Thank you for believing in me, supporting my visions, and for following me to Maui. Thank you for the interior book layout and cover design of this book. Your many talents continue to amaze me. I look forward to spending forever together in paradise. I love you!

To my sons, Sam and Jacob: I am so proud of the young men that you have both become. I am honored to share the same last name. I encourage you both to follow your passions for a lifetime, and wherever you end up, that is where you are meant to be. I love you both and you make me very proud.

To my parents, Jack and Lois: Thank you for believing in me and for exposing me to entrepreneurship at such a young age. You have both taught me more than you realize and I will be forever grateful. I love you both and am so very grateful for the many sacrifices you each made throughout the years.

"I am always doing
what I can not do yet,
in order to learn
how to do it."

– Vincent van Gogh

ACKNOWLEDGMENTS

Kevin Allen, Dave Angelo, Dave Beauchamp, Cory Bouck, Richard Branson, Les Brown, Theresa Callahan-Evans, Bryan Caplovitz, Bettina Carey, Lori Chaffin, Jesus Christ, Taylor Clark, James Donaldson, Brent Duskin, Bob Erdman, Al Foxx, Susan Friedmann, Rick Frommer, Tracie Fujikane, Nicole Gabriel, Brodi Goshi, Mark Victor Hansen, Michael Helgeson, Ray Higdon, Jeff Hodges, Howard Howell, Nancy Jacques, Dan Janal, Jerry Jenkins, Steve Jobs, Jake Kevorkian, Kevin Knebl, Og Mandino, Mark Matteson, John C. Maxwell, Bill McCarrick, Albert Mensah, Mother Teresa, Kieran Murry, Sherri Murry, Friedrich Nietzsche, Larry Olsen, Suze Orman, Kate Phillips, Tim Polk, Dan Poynter, Frank Reed, Jim Rohn, Shiloh Schroeder, Molly Shumway, Brandy Lokelani Sinoto, Val Smyth, Jack Snow, Jacob Snow, Lois Snow, Margaret Snow, Sam Snow, Tim Snow, W. Clement Stone, Chris Tew, Brian Tracy, Rob Van Pelt, Tobin Van Pelt, Nick Vujicic, Tony Wall, Mary West, and Zig Ziglar.

I also would like to thank Tyler Tichelaar for his amazing editing skills. Without his talent, this book would just be an incomplete Word document on my laptop.

CONTENTS

" You can fail at what you don't want,
so you might as well take a chance
at doing what you love."

– Jim Carrey

A NOTE TO PARENTS

I believe the earlier in life you start earning your own money, the more success you will achieve over the course of your lifetime. Therefore, I am a huge proponent of Girl Scouts selling cookies, young student-athletes selling raffle tickets to support their teams, kids doing household chores, and anything that teaches a kid the value of money (and the sacrifice in time and / or smarts to earn it).

I purposely did NOT write this book as a kids' book! Why? Because kids don't buy books! They often don't have any money, and they are doing things they enjoy way more than reading (such as video games, texting, YouTube, playing sports, hanging out with friends—anything but reading). Maybe even climbing trees? I'm not sure whether kids do that anymore. I used to love to climb trees as a kid. I was the same way as kids today (except for video games and YouTube) and never bought or read a book as a kid. Now I am a best-selling author. Go figure.

Prior to college, I don't think I read a book for enjoyment. In school when I was assigned a book report, I would only read the back cover of the book in preparation for writing the report. Like kids today, I had other things to do that more thoroughly caught my attention. Then I got hooked by inspirational books at nineteen years old and have read a couple of thousand of them since then (and I plan to read many more in the future).

Early on, I learned firsthand the importance of earning money for myself. My parents gave me a "fishing pole" (so to speak) when they said, "Patrick, you can have anything you want in life as long as you earn it and purchase it with your own money." I will never forget this lesson. I am hopeful your parents did the same for you.

So there I was becoming an entrepreneur in the seventh grade, taking on a *Detroit Free Press* newspaper route and delivering 50 daily papers and 150 Sunday papers every morning from 5 to 7 a.m. before school and on the weekends. I did this for a year or more. Then, during the snowy winters, I shoveled driveways as a way to earn extra money and made $10 to $20 per house. In the summer, I pushed my dad's lawnmower around from house-to-house, knocking on doors of homes with long grass to ask whether I could mow their grass...and BAM...thirty minutes later, another $20 bill was in my pocket (not bad money considering it was the early 1980s).

Then I got smart and realized it was better to earn money with my mind, my heart, my voice, and my sheer will of perseverance. So I traded in the manual labor of my *Detroit Free Press* paper route to another guy and got into sales by selling *Detroit Free Press* subscriptions door-to-door in the eighth grade on Tuesday and Thursday nights from 6 to 9:30 p.m. No more waking up at 4:30 a.m., and the money was five times better! I would get dropped off (in various neighborhoods near my hometown of Owosso, Michigan, by the old guy who worked for the newspaper's sales department) and then go door-to-door selling subscriptions.

When I sold a Sunday subscription, I would earn a $1, a daily $2, and if I hit a home run and sold daily and Sunday combined, I would earn $3. My sales pitch was that there were more than $5 worth of coupons in each Sunday paper and it also included a *TV Guide*. So almost every house that had someone home to answer the door turned into a $1 commission in my pocket.

This job was so much fun, and I was earning $80

to $100 per night (a lot of money for a kid back in 1983). At the time, I was into bike racing, so I saved up $600 and purchased a Team Fuji racing bike, and I was off riding all over the Michigan countryside. After graduating from high school and having a college football career-ending back injury, I sold this bike to buy skis when I transferred to the University of Montana, only later to regret selling my prized racing bike. Thirty years later on Craigslist, I bought the exact same year bike, make, model, size, color, everything the same...and today, it is one of my prized possessions. Kind of like my own entrepreneurship trophy (and it is proudly displayed in my home office).

Several years later, using these same entrepreneurial skills, I had one guy offer me the title to his 1968 Ford Mustang coupe in trade for my publishing coaching services. This was a no-brainer, so I executed the trade. I fixed up the Mustang and then decided to trade it for my high school dream car. All the way through high school, I had a poster on my bedroom wall of a Guards Red 1986 Porsche 944 Turbo that I dreamed of one day owning. But how was a teenager ever to own such an expensive vehicle, right? That is what I was thinking too. But I held on to the vision, and twenty-eight years later, I traded my newly acquired Mustang for, you guessed it, a Guards Red 1986 Porsche 944 Turbo. I have since restored this vehicle to mint condition and it too serves as an entrepreneurial trophy (another vision realized over time). By no means am I trying to impress anyone with this car; for goodness sake, it is now almost thirty years old. What is most impressive to me is holding onto the vision for thirty years, never giving up on my dream, and then eventually realizing this vision and making it come true as a result of my entrepreneurial pursuits. This is the exact concept that I share in this book (holding onto a vision, never giving up, and making it become real)!

Today, as a result of the lessons I learned as a "boy entrepreneur," I have become an international best-selling author with several books, a professional keynote speaker (having done more than 2,500 engagements on three continents all over the world), a publishing, book marketing, and professional speaking coach with more than 750 clients, and an Internet entrepreneur. I have been featured as a cover story in *USA TODAY* and featured in *Forbes* and *The New York Times* (and many other newspapers and magazines) all by being interviewed on the subject matter of "entrepreneurship."

Although I am not a "hero," I am a "learner," and I

just communicate what I learn. I am not there yet. I am still a work in progress, still uncovering answers to life's biggest questions. In fact, I suspect I can learn more from you than you can from me!

After two layoffs in 2001 and again in 2002, eventually, I quit my last job and retired at thirty-six years old from the corporate world. I have been self-employed as a full-time entrepreneur ever since. In telling my story, I am not trying to impress you in any way; I only want to impress upon you that the key to breaking the dependence on "working for the man" is to start early and learn these entrepreneurial skills at a young age, so that later on, you can be in complete control of both your time and your financial destiny.

As a result of becoming an entrepreneur at twelve years old, I have been able to navigate my career successfully on my own terms instead of being manipulated, directed, and underpaid by an employer. I started working from home early in my career, better allowing me to raise my two boys with their dad in the home and also to coach many of their sports teams. Additionally, because of being an entrepreneur, once both my boys graduated from high school, I was finally able to make good on a goal set twenty-six years previously, which was to move to Maui, Hawai`i. I have achieved my goal and plan to live here the rest of my life. Had I not been an entre-preneur, calling my own shots, I would still be at the mercy of an employer, forcing me to live where my bosses felt I could best serve their goals. No thank you! Maui is much better! I can assure you of that.

Why do I share all this with you? Well, I believe, as the parent of two boys (actually young men now in their early twenties...Sam Snow and Jacob Snow), the absolute best gift you can give your children is not money, not material things, but to give them your time, your work ethic, and "a fishing pole" so they can learn to fish for themselves. Both of my boys have been entrepreneurs for years, and both, consequently, are doing very well financially with their college educations and in their careers, so I am very proud of both of them.

I am pleased that my sons have become indepen-dent and are proud of their work ethic that has been passed down through many generations. At sixteen, my grandfather, Emil Snow, was a bit untruthful about his age so he could get a full-time job in an automobile factory (Buick) in Flint, Michigan (two years before he could legally work there at age eighteen); he then spent forty years there providing for his family. Then upon retirement, he became an accountant and got into local politics. My father, Jack Snow, was a schoolteacher for forty years, all the while coaching multiple sports. During the summers, he worked in construction and did roofing. He taught me the value of working with him doing roofing jobs in the hot sun before I was the legal age to work. Both my father and grandfather and their hard work had an impact on me, and I would like to think that I passed this same dedication to providing for oneself to my two boys while they were growing up. Instead of them going out and working minimum wage jobs, they opted to buy both paintball guns and Nike SB shoes at wholesale on the Internet, and then turn around and flip them at retail prices about $50-150 higher, earning them both far more than any minimum wage job ever could. Better yet, they did it around their school and sports schedules, with the only tools being a laptop computer and an Internet connection.

Hence I challenge you, too, to teach your children and grandchildren to fish for themselves as early in life as you can. You will be pleased that you did. Better yet, buy them fishing poles and help them research where the fish are biting.

A couple of side notes to share before we begin. I am sorry if my title offends you in any way. That was not my intention. "Girl Entrepreneur dot com" was not available, so I could only secure "Boy Entrepreneur dot com." Next, if you notice that the majority of mentors in this book are men, I would ask you to look past that and focus on the mentor's message (and not his or her sex). I believe the message of this book will impact your son or daughter (or grandson or granddaughter) equally, regardless of gender.

By the way, I did manage to secure "Gal Entrepreneur dot com" recently, so when this book is a success, I will certainly write a sequel to it.

Now get out there and buy some fishing poles, help your child sell some Girl Scout cookies, play a game of Monopoly with your kids (or grandkids), or even a game of chess...whatever it takes! Let's team up together and help the kids of today become the leaders of tomorrow!

Enjoy this book and share it with your children and grandchildren....

GIVING THE GIFT OF WISDOM

Which of these three options best describes you?

Your boss is an idiot! You work with a bunch of stiffs! You can't stand your job! You get no respect and far too little pay for your level of experience and expertise. You are living paycheck-to-paycheck and the money runs out before the month does. You can't sleep at night and have ulcer-producing anxiety trying to figure out how you are going to stave off financial devastation in today's challenging economy, and you know that taking on a second job is not the solution. You are fed up and you have no idea where to turn.

Or...You are in school (junior high, high school, or college) and are trying to figure out a better way to make it in today's ultra-competitive environment. You see your parents go off to work each day to dead-end jobs that they always complain about while they lack money. As a result, you are determined to make a better life for yourself and your future, but you don't know where to turn or what is the best career advice to follow.

Or...You are a successful entrepreneur, completely content with your career choices and on track to achieve your financial goals, or perhaps you are already retired (or soon to be).

I suspect that you fall into the third category, and you are thinking of getting multiple copies of this book for all your children and / or grandchildren. Great idea! If you fit into any one of these three categories, congratulations! You will enjoy this book, and hopefully, the surprise ending will keep you thinking long after you put this book down.

NOTE: This is *not* a children's book (but children will enjoy it). This book is not just for boys. *Boy Entrepreneur* is a book that men and women, boys and girls, young and old—anyone who is not satisfied with mediocrity and looking to get ahead in his or her life and career—can benefit from when he or she applies the proven principles shared in this story. This book was written with the intent that you should read it and share it by giving it to your kids or grandkids to read.

I purposely made this book short (and in a bigger font point size) with the intention that you can read it in a few hours or less. Also, I wrote it in the form of a fable since stories are the best and most exciting way to learn and often their lessons are more memorable. Although this book is considered inspirational fiction, some of it is based on real events that actually occurred in one way or another. Better yet, many of these events may eventually occur in your life once you predetermine your destination in life and then take massive action.

There is an old saying, "Give a man a fish and he eats for a day, but teach a man how to fish and he eats for a lifetime." This concept is so true. So allow this book to become a "fishing pole" for you, your children, or grandchildren to use to learn how to succeed in business and life.

Regardless of your age or gender, we all have the need financially to provide for ourselves, our family, our future, which is why this topic of "entrepreneurship" is so very important. My recipe is to take an inventory of both your talents and passions, and then transform your "most-marketable passion" into your profession. This is my challenge to you. Simply put, I challenge you to follow your dreams! Let's face it: either you follow your own dreams, or you spend the rest of your life working for someone who did!

There is an old saying, "If you grow up wealthy, you die poor. If you grow up poor, you die wealthy." This is kind of a "Catch-22." So why is this? Some of my friends came from middle-class families like me; we worked our tails off earning our own money, saving our own money, and buying our own stuff. This hard-work ethic stuck for a lifetime and many of my childhood friends are doing very well today.

Conversely, my friends who came from very wealthy families and had parents who bought them anything and everything they wanted, never had jobs when they were younger. Unfortunately, some of these folks developed an "entitlement mentality," and never learned how to earn their own money for themselves or learned the value of hard work. As a result, many of these folks have eventually been cut off from their parents, often turning to drugs and alcohol and never graduating from college; they may end up in the category of one day "dying poor." I hope not since these folks are my friends and are good people; they just never learned to fish for themselves, ever! And so now they will spend the rest of their days being hungry and dependent.

So how can you teach kids and adults who grew up in both types of families to succeed in business? The answer is to study, learn, and apply the lessons shared in the very last section of this book: "50 Greatest Sales & Marketing Secrets for Entrepreneurs." You will love the inspirational story of Ikaika Marks (the main character in this book), but this last section is where you can take the book's lessons and apply them to your business immediately to see large payoffs. I saved the best for last, so make sure you read this book all the way to the end to benefit from this added bonus (and the other Special Reports).

However, life to me is about more than creating wealth; it is all about family! All about teaching the youth of today to become the leaders of tomorrow. I suspect you feel the same way. An old quote says, "Children are like banks. The more time you put in with them, the greater the return will be on your investment of time." So your kids and grandkids don't need money; they need and crave your time, your skills, your intellectual knowledge, your work ethic, and perhaps most importantly, your love. So don't be afraid to show and tell them that you love them. Even today, every phone call with my boys (who are now men) ends with "I love you and I am proud of you!" I challenge you to say the same.

So what does all this mean to you? You are holding a

fable, and inside this story is a series of thought-provoking quotes that have the ability to change your life (and the lives of your family), if you apply the lessons the main character, Ikaika, learns to your life! If you can do that, you will forever benefit.

What will you get by applying these lessons? You, your children, and your grandchildren will learn how to become pioneering leaders. You will learn how to harness the power of vision into the realization of your dreams. You will learn how to transform your obstacles into opportunities. You will learn the secret to attaining lifelong happiness. You will learn to overcome rejection, expand your comfort zone, never give up, think for yourself, follow your dreams, earn your own money, and keep it too. You will learn that family is the most important thing in the world, and perhaps you will even learn a thing or two about faith. You will learn that if a twelve-year-old kid can earn his own money and follow his dreams, you can too!

Dr. Robert Brooks says this about kids: "One of the most important factors that contributes to the resilience in children is the presence of at least one person in their lives who believes in them." I challenge you to be that person in a kid's life by sharing and reading this book with a kid in need.

Julius Segal has said that kids need a "charismatic adult from which they can gather strength." I challenge you to be that person in a kid's life by sharing and reading this book with a kid in need.

Forest Whitcraft once said: "One hundred years from now it will not matter what my bank account was, or the sort of house I lived in, or the kind of car I drove. But the world may be different because I was important in the life of a child." I challenge you to be that person in a kid's life by sharing and reading this book to a kid in need.

Are you ready to come to Hawai`i and walk a mile in the shoes of a twelve-year-old budding entrepreneur? Are you ready to make your own money and fish for yourself? Are you ready to be the director of your life's play, become the captain of your ship, and the creator of your destiny?

If so, let's enjoy this inspirational fable together, so that you, your children, and your grandchildren can unleash the "Boy Entrepreneur" spirit in your life, your business, your family, and your future. Are you ready to begin? Good, let's go. Your destiny begins now. This is your time, so let's get started.

Chapter 1

DOING HOMEWORK

When Ikaika Marks was born, his parents gave him a Hawaiian name that means "strong and powerful." Ikaika often wondered why they chose that name for him. One day he asked his father, "Why did you name me Ikaika?" His father replied, "It's because you are strong enough to succeed at anything in life if you want it enough." Ikaika often thought about his father's words and wondered whether they would come true. He little suspected they would when he was twelve years old, the summer after he completed sixth grade.

Many of Ikaika's friends had a hard time pronouncing his name, so soon he began to be called "Kaika" (for short), and that's what everyone called him from that time forward. (Except, of course, his mother, whenever he got in trouble.)

Kaika had many friends in his neighborhood whom he grew up with and hung out with day and night.

Included in his group of friends was a neighbor girl, Leilani, whom he had a crush on. Leilani's name in Hawaiian means "girl from heaven."

Kaika had lived his whole life on the Hawaiian island of Maui located in the middle of the Pacific Ocean. Maui is centrally located between the United States mainland to the east, Japan and China to the west, and Australia and New Zealand to the southwest. He lived in the city of Wailuku located right next to Kahului in the middle of Maui.

Kaika was an only child and he lived with his mother and grandmother. His mother was from Hawai`i as well, but his father was from the mainland. Kaika was sad because his father was in the military and he had recently been stationed overseas. His father was from Boston and an avid Red Sox fan. Kaika and his father used to play catch in the park for hours, so it was no surprise that he loved baseball so much. However, football was his favorite sport since he loved the toughness of the sport and the opportunity it gave him to grow as a leader.

That summer, Kaika's sixth grade teacher, Mr. Goshi, had assigned him to return back to school in the fall with a two-page paper for his seventh grade teacher about anything important he learned over the summer. Mr. Goshi told Kaika and his classmates, "I want you to experience a summer like no other. I want you to have fun, but also to *read, think, dream,* and *write.* I want you to remember what President Abraham Lincoln once said:

"You become what you think about."

EXERCISE:

Write in the five projects or homework assignments in your life (or business) that you have been procrastinating on for some time, and that if you committed yourself to completing, would allow you to experience amazing growth in your life, relationships, and finances. List them here with the dates you will complete them.

PROJECT   DATE

1._____ _____

2._____ _____

3._____ _____

4._____ _____

5._____ _____

- Chapter 2 -

ASKING FOR HELP

On this particular summer day, playing with his friends under the banyan tree, Kaika was sad. His Maui Little League baseball team had won the state tournament, and now Kaika and his teammates had an opportunity to travel to California for the Little League Western Regional Playoffs. This was a week-long tournament to be held in San Bernadino, California.

However, in order for the team to make the trip, each player needed to come up with $500 for airfare and hotel expenses. The Maui Little League could pay $1,000 for each player, but another $500 per player would need to be raised or earned to ensure that each team member could make the trip. After several carwash fundraisers, it appeared that neither Kaika nor many of his teammates would have enough money to go so he was hopeful Coach Bill would come up with a solution.

When Kaika asked his mother and grandmother whether they could just pay for the trip, they both explained that they could not afford it. They were both waitresses at the local Tasty Crust pancake house, and they simply didn't make enough money to pay the rent, buy groceries, and still have money left over for a baseball trip to California. His mother was glad Kaika asked, though, since she was quick to remind him of one of her favorite quotes she learned from the book *Chicken Soup for the Soul* that was constantly on her bed stand:

**"You must A-S-K to G-E-T!
If you don't ask, you won't get."**

But Kaika had asked, and he had not gotten what he wanted. As a result, Kaika was very sad and he did not feel that life was fair. No matter how hard he thought about it, he could not think of a way he could make the trip to California. He really wanted to go, but he had no idea how to earn the required $500 to make the trip with his teammates.

That week, the team parents called a meeting to discuss the trip and vote on whether or not to send their team to California. They still had several weeks before the deadline. Therefore, it was recommended that each parent go home and encourage his or her son to find some kind of summer work to help pay for his airline ticket, hotel, and transportation.

EXERCISE:

Who are five people in your life to whom you could reach out and "ASK" for help if needed? Better yet, who are five people you know who perhaps may need your help at the present time but are too shy to ask? What can you do to help them?

1._____

2._____

3._____

4._____

5._____

- Chapter 3 -

FOCUSING ON LIFE'S MANY BLESSINGS

The next evening as Kaika and his friends rode their bikes to Kahului to play wiffle ball under the banyan tree, they noticed a group of tourists walking back from the grocery store. The tourists passed the banyan tree on their way back to the cruise ship that was in port for the weekend.

Every Sunday morning at eight o'clock for as long as Kaika could remember, a huge cruise ship would pull into Kahului, Maui harbor, and stay until Monday night around six o'clock. Each week, the ship brought nearly 3,000 tourists to Maui from all over the world. On this particular Sunday evening, Kaika and his friends noticed one of the tourists could barely walk and used a crutch. As the tourist approached Kaika and his friends under the banyan tree, he yelled, "Why are these birds making so much noise?" Kaika replied, "Every night around dusk, thousands of myna birds return to their banyan trees for the night, and just before they go to sleep, they 'talk story' by sharing their adventures from the day with the other birds." The tourist laughed, and with a slur in his voice, he said, "These birds would be better off just checking into a hotel, don't you think?"

When Kaika laughed, the tourist asked, "What is your name, young man?" Kaika replied, "My name is Kaika and this tree is their hotel! What is your name, and where are you from?" The tourist said, "My name is Al and I live in Seattle." Kaika then asked, "Why do you talk funny and have to walk with a cane?" Al replied. "When I was a teenager, I was in a motorcycle accident. As a result, I am paralyzed on one side of my body." Kaika replied, "Is life depressing knowing you are going to spend the rest of your life talking with a slur, barely being able to walk, and being half-paralyzed?" "Of course not," replied Al. "I am happy as can be!"

Al's words reminded Kaika that he was sad. He said, "Well, I am not very happy at all. I am sad because my father is away in the military, and my mom can't afford to send me with my team to the baseball tournament in California!" Al looked at Kaika for a moment, and then he said, "Kaika, let me share with you the secret to my happiness. The secret is to:

"Focus on what you have, not what you don't have!"

You have your friends, you still have your mother (whom I am sure you love very much), and you have the beautiful surroundings of Maui, this banyan tree, these birds, the blue ocean, the rainbows, and I bet you have many other reasons to be happy. Kaika, I challenge you to focus on what you have, not on what you don't!" As Al limped away with his cane in hand, he yelled out, "And one more thing: stay away from motorcycles!" Kaika smiled, waved goodbye to Al, and knew he truly was blessed to meet Al that day. He decided from then on that he would focus on his blessings, instead of the things he did not have. Also Kaika was so inspired by this quote that he decided to start a quote journal that evening when he got home. His mother's and Al's quote would be the first entries.

EXERCISE:

What are three of your most important blessings?

1._____

2._____

3._____

Chapter 4

TAKING ADVANTAGE OF OPPORTUNITIES

The following Sunday afternoon, Kaika and his friends were again playing wiffle ball beneath their favorite banyan tree when another tourist approached them. The man asked whether he could throw a few pitches with Kaika and his friends. This man had an enormous smile on his face, and he seemed genuinely interested in tossing a few pitches at the boys and Leilani to try to strike them out.

As they played, the man said, "My name is Albert. It is a blessing to be here in Maui! You kids are so lucky to live here. What are your names?" Leilani and the boys all gave him their names, and Kaika, who was the last to respond, said, "My name is Kaika. Where are you from Albert?" Albert replied, "I am originally from Accra, Ghana (in West Africa), but I am an 'opportunist,' so I travel all over the world speaking about opportunities." Immediately, Kaika asked, "What is an opportunist?" Albert replied:

"An opportunist
is someone who turns his obstacles and
adversities into new opportunities!"

Then Albert said, "Let me give you an example. What obstacles are you faced with, Kaika?" Kaika replied, "My baseball team won the Maui regional tournament, and now I am trying to figure out a way to raise $500 to go play the next tournament in California." "That's great!" said Albert. "So what is the problem?" Kaika responded, "I can't go because my mother and grandmother can't afford to pay my way!"

Albert thought about this statement for a moment and then he said, "Do you see this cruise ship behind me? It is full of 3,000 opportunities for you to raise money for your trip." "How so?" asked Kaika. "Growing up in Ghana," said Albert, "I was always selling things to people who walked by on the street. You can do the same here in Maui if you can find something the tourists can't purchase anywhere else that will remind them of their visit to Maui."

Kaika immediately smiled. An idea had suddenly come into his mind. This idea, if thoroughly executed, would solve Kaika's dilema.

Albert now started walking toward the Whole Foods grocery store across Hana Highway. As he left, he waved and said, "Good luck to you, Kaika, and remember: Turn your obstacles into opportunities and always dance to the beat of your own drums!"

EXERCISE:

What are five obstacles and adversities that are currently challenging you in your life that may actually turn out to be opportunities in disguise? List them here and then make a decision to overcome each one. In doing so, you will become unstoppable!

1._____

2._____

3._____

4._____

5._____

OWNING THE VISION

As soon as Albert left, Kaika noticed some other tourists on the other side of the huge banyan tree visiting with a guy who had pulled up in his van towing a trailer full of mopeds. It appeared that this business owner was taking advantage of the foot traffic from the cruise ships by renting out mopeds to them. This activity caught Kaika's attention so he walked up to learn more.

As soon as Kaika walked up, he saw the owner of the moped company was busy helping a woman pick out the right moped for her. As a result, Kaika met her husband, who had already picked out his moped.

The guy standing next to his moped said, "Excuse me; my name is Larry. I am wondering if you can help us out by telling us whether there is somewhere nearby that we can take in the beautiful Maui scenery? And by the way, what is your name?"

Kaika replied, "Yes, of course. My name is Kaika, and you just take this Hana highway due west up through old town Wailuku and it will take you back up into the Iao Valley where you will see some of the most beautiful mountains in all of Hawai`i. You will also see the 'Iao Needle,' a majestic mountain peak that shoots up 1,200 feet straight into the sky from the valley below. It is a mass of land that looks like a tall needle as all the land around it has eroded away." Kaika continued, "In 1790, the Battle of Kepaniwai took place there, in which Kamehameha the Great defeated Kalanikupule and the Maui army during his campaign to unify the Hawaiian Islands." Larry replied, "Wow, Kaika! You sure do know a lot about Maui! You should be a tour guide." "Nope," Kaika replied. "I would rather hang out with my friends. But I am thinking about starting a business—only I really don't know how to get started or what I am doing. Can you offer me any advice?" Larry replied, "Yes, I can. I live in Arizona where I am an author, speaker, and corporate consultant on the topic of 'vision.' My advice is to live by this mantra:

"You have no right to work on the 'how' until you can taste, touch, smell, feel, hear, emotionalize, and 'own the vision.' The vision comes first and then you see 'how' to accomplish your goals."

"In other words, Kaika, once you learn to 'own your vision,' your 'how' will slowly appear over time. This is the key to succeeding in business!" Kaika responded, "Wow, thank you, Larry! I am going to learn to *own my vision,* and as I own my vision, my business will present itself slowly in a physical reality. Is that right?" Larry responded, "Yes. Well, I've got to run; my wife Diane is ready to dash away on her moped so I must catch up to her. Good luck, Kaika!"

With this new bit of wisdom, Kaika headed home. He now felt more determined than ever to create a business so he could earn money to participate in his baseball team's trip to California.

As Kaika fell asleep that night in his bed, his mind was busy visualizing all the ways he could be a success in business.

EXERCISE:

Describe your new business idea below:

_____

_____

_____

- *Chapter 6* -

LEARNING FROM GRANDPARENTS

The next morning upon awakening, Kaika had an idea based on a vision he had dreamed about the night before. He immediately ran into his mom's bedroom to share his plan of carving makau fishhooks and selling them at the Saturday morning swap meet in Kahului and under the banyan trees on Sunday and Monday as the cruise ship passengers walked by.

Before Kaika's grandfather had passed away, he had taught Kaika how to use a knife to carve the wood they found in the West Maui Mountains. Kaika's grandfather used to carve tikis so he taught his grandson how to carve. Grandpa had a makau fishhook on a necklace that he always wore around his neck.

After thinking about his plan all day, that evening at dinner, Kaika asked his grandmother the significance of this Hawaiian fishhook and why Grandpa had always worn it. Grandma replied, "The ancient Hawaiians created these makau fishhooks out of any materials they could find. The makau fishhook represents all that is good, and it ensures that whoever wears it will achieve prosperity since it symbolizes both strength and good luck."

She went on to say: "Your grandfather worked for forty years for the Hawaiian Commercial & Sugar Company before retiring at fifty-eight years old.

Once he retired, he worked part-time with a network marketing company and also carved tikis to make extra money for our family.

He came home one night after a "Super Saturday Conference" with a quote from an unknown author on a sheet of paper and asked me to give this sheet of paper to you when you started on your journey of earning money for yourself."

Kaika opened up the folded note to see what it said. He felt blessed to gain the following wisdom from his grandfather, in his grandpa's writing:

**"If you want what others have,
you must do what others have done,
and you will get what others have gotten!"**

Kaika was so amazed by both his grandpa's quote and the mystique of the makau fishhook. He just knew he could take the carving skills his grandfather had taught him and create his own fishhook necklaces to sell to the tourists who visited Maui each week. He immediately copied this quote from his grandfather into his quote journal. Over the next week, Kaika carved ten makaus out of the prized koa wood his grandfather and he had found in the mountains. In the storage shed in the backyard, he found some hemp string his grandfather had left behind. Finally, Kaika's mother suggested he stain the makaus with lacquer to make them waterproof against the salt water and give them a bright shine.

EXERCISE:

What are the three greatest lessons in life that you have learned from your mother, father, grandmother, or grandfather? Write these lessons below and then pass this wisdom down to your children and grand-children. Not only should you share these lessons with your family but also with your friends.

1._____

2._____

3._____

Chapter 7

CREATING THE PRODUCT OR SERVICE

Kaika could not wait for Saturday and Sunday to come. Saturday, he planned to sell his makau Hawaiian fishhook necklaces at the Kahului Swap Meet, and on Sunday and Monday, he would sell them to the cruise ship tourists. He planned on selling three days a week and carving new inventory the other four days a week.

Finally, Saturday came. Kaika woke at 6 a.m. and carried his ten makaus in a light blue milk crate he had found in his backyard, along with a white beach towel he pulled off the clothesline.

Upon arrival at the swap meet, he paid his fifty cents admission to enter the gate. He then proceeded down the entry ramp and found a spot of soft green grass. He emptied his milk crate of the ten makau fishhook necklaces, flipped over his milk crate, placed the white towel over the milk crate to create a nice looking, small sales presentation table, and then displayed his ten makau necklaces that he had hand-carved. Next, he pulled a small sign out of his back pocket made from a cardboard cereal box at home. On it, he had written with black marker:

Makau Fishhook Necklaces for Sale: $25

After about ten minutes or so, an older woman, who was one of the officials running the swap meet, quickly approached Kaika. She said, "Young man, you cannot sell your makaus here! You need to purchase a booth under one of those white tents. In order for you to buy your sales booth, you need to have a business license. And to get a business license, you need to be eighteen years old. You are going to have to gather these items up and leave the swap meet since you are not allowed to sell inside here. Besides, no one wants to buy necklaces that were made by a kid. They won't think they're very good quality."

Kaika immediately frowned, packed up his sales display, and walked out the gate. As he walked out, he remembered his father telling him that the reason why he was named "Ikaika" was because he was "strong and powerful." This thought stuck with him as he walked off, and he felt that perhaps all hope was not lost because the cruise ship was coming into port tomorrow, so he would have another shot at selling his makau necklaces.

Nonetheless, Kaika was still pretty down on himself and unsure whether his plan would work.

EXERCISE:

What are five of your most marketable passions that you think you could develop into a product or service and take to market as an entrepreneur?

1._____

2._____

3._____

4._____

5._____

Chapter 8

RISING AGAINST ADVERSITY

On the way home, Kaika remembered that his mother had asked him to stop at Long's Drugstore and buy a can of Spam for dinner. So he crossed the Hana Highway, went into the store, and bought some Spam and some white chocolate chip macadamia nut cookies for dessert.

While waiting in line, he overheard a man speaking in a thick accent in another language. Meeting someone from a foreign country intrigued Kaika, so he asked the man, "Excuse me, sir. What language are you speaking and where are you from?" The man replied, "I am from Naumburg, Germany, and I am speaking the German language."

Kaika asked, "What is your name and what do you do for a living?" The man replied, "My name is Friedrich and I am a teacher and philosopher. I am here on vacation in Maui teaching a summer course at the University of Hawai`i's Maui campus." Kaika asked, "Since you're a philosopher, what advice can you offer a kid who is going through a tough time?"

Friedrich replied, "Tough times make for even tougher people. I would ask you to remember this quote for a lifetime. It will guide you through lots of healing and adversities:

**"That which does not kill you,
strengthens you!"**

Kaika said, "Thank you. I will remember this advice!" He then took the Spam, cookies, and his sales receipt and headed out the door for home to plan his strategy for tomorrow.

Kaika was not about to give up. He was determined to succeed the next day selling under the banyan tree.

Kaika's grandfather often shared with him how challenging things were back in the day. He figured that if his grandfather persevered, so could he. Kaika decided he would not give up.

EXERCISE:

What are the five greatest adversities in your life that you have overcome?

1._____

2._____

3._____

4._____

5._____

Chapter 9

OVERCOMING ALL OBSTACLES

Kaika decided to go the long way home along the sandy beach so he could reflect on what had happened at the swap meet. His brilliant idea was not working out, so he did not know how he was going to raise the money for his trip. He was even considering calling up Coach Bill to ask for help.

As he walked along the beach, he approached an old man and his Poi dog. The dog was fetching a stick that the old man was throwing into the ocean. Kaika watched the dog for a minute and then the old man introduced himself.

The old man said, "Young man, my name is Og. Please tell me why you have such a sad face." Kaika replied, "I had the great idea of selling my makau fishhook necklaces at the swap meet, but I was told I could not sell my items there because I am not old enough and I didn't have a business license. I am not sure what to do now. I am concerned that I may not be able to raise the money needed so I can go with my baseball team to a tournament in California."

Og said, "Don't give up! There is always a way. Everything worthwhile in life takes time and requires perseverance and an unwavering belief in yourself." Kaika asked, "Well, then, what do you think I should do?"

Og replied, "Let me give you some advice that will help you earn lots of money in your life and, more importantly, will allow you to provide a better living for both you and your family for many years to come:

"Obstacles are necessary for success because in selling, as in all careers of importance, victory only comes after many struggles and countless defeats!"

With this newfound wisdom in his mind, Kaika thanked Og and continued to walk home. He now had a smile on his face and felt more eager than ever to sell his first makau the very next morning under the banyan tree. With this great advice, Kaika felt much better about things. When he got home, he grabbed his skimboard, and he and Leilani spent the rest of the day enjoying the surf at Sugar Beach.

EXERCISE:

Identify the five biggest roadblocks or obstacles that currently stand in your way. What actions can you take to eliminate them, go around them, through them, or over them?

1._____

2._____

3._____

4._____

5._____

- Chapter 10 -

IGNORING NEGATIVE PEOPLE

On Sunday morning, Kaika woke at seven o'clock. He rode his bike down to the banyan tree at the end of the parking lot where the passengers would exit the ship on their way to the grocery store located across the Hana highway. Strapped to his bike was his milk crate and ten makau fishhook necklaces wrapped safely in a white towel.

When the ship docked at eight o'clock, Kaika was in position and ready to sell his ten necklaces. Soon, hundreds of tourists began to walk past his homemade display stand made from an upside-down milk crate with a white beach towel for a tablecloth.

One older man stopped with his daughter to buy her a necklace. The older man asked, "Young boy, what is your name?" Kaika replied, "My name is Kaika, and I am trying to raise money to pay for my baseball trip to California. What is your name and where are you from?" The older man said, "My name is Les and I was born and raised in Miami, but now I live in Chicago. I am a radio host, author, and speaker."

Les reached into his wallet and pulled out a crisp, brand new $100 bill and said, "I will take two makau necklaces for $50." Then as Kaika racked his brains trying to think how he could make change for a $100 bill, Les said, "Son, you can keep the $50 in change!"

Kaika smiled as if he had just won the lottery. He now had a crisp $100 bill in his pocket. Les was known for being a big tipper.

Les then said to him, "According to my travel book, Maui also has a swap meet every Saturday here in Kahului; you should sell your makau necklaces there also." Kaika replied, "Yes, I tried that yesterday, but I was kicked out because I was told I am too young and I do not have a business license!"

Les replied, "Son...you gotta be HUNGRY! Let me share with you the most important wisdom my grade school teacher, Mr. Jackson, once taught me:

**"Never, under any circumstances,
let someone else's opinion of you
determine your reality!"**

"Therefore, next Saturday, get there early and set up your sales stand just outside of the swap meet's front entrance in the grass area next to the parking lot. You can then sell your necklaces outside the entrance gate without a license, regardless of your age!" Kaika thanked Les for his advice, and the next week, he did set up his booth outside the swap meet's entrance. But he did not make a single sale! Then on Sunday, he again attempted to sell his makau necklaces under the banyan tree to the cruise ship tourists. By the end of that weekend, he still had made only one sale (the $100 worth of his creations to Les from the cruise ship the previous weekend). He was getting quite discouraged and wondered whether he could ever raise the required $400 more to go on the trip. Furthermore, he had just been elected team captain for his trip to California, so he was questioning his leadership skills, especially if he could not be successful selling his creations.

EXERCISE:

List the three most positive people in your life?

1._____

2._____

3._____

- Chapter 11 -

BECOMING THE LEADER

That Sunday night after sitting for both Saturday and all day on Sunday without making a single sale, Kaika was getting even more discouraged about the possibility of his business becoming successful. He was encouraged about being selected as team captain, but he had lots of questions about this role, especially because he had never been a leader before.

As he rode his bike home along the Hana Highway heading toward Wailuku, he noticed hundreds and hundreds of people standing in line attempting to enter the War Memorial Gymnasium.

There were also hundreds of cars searching for parking spots, and it appeared that all the spots had been taken. Kaika's curiosity got the better of him so he locked up his bike against the fence and wandered over to see what the event was all about.

Kaika had no plans that night so he too got in line to find out why everyone was waiting. As he joined the line, he asked the guy in front of him. "What are all these people doing out here waiting in line?"

The gentleman in front of him replied, "Nick, the famous inspirational speaker from Australia, is speaking tonight inside the gymnasium, and it is pretty obvious that none of us is going to make it into the event since the lines are just not moving. Nick was born with no arms and no legs, and his videos are all over the Internet."

Kaika responded, "Well, why are you here to hear him speak? What can you learn from such a speaker? And what is your name, and where are you from?"

The gentleman replied, "My name is John and I am from California. I too am a speaker, an author, and a leadership guru. I am here in Maui hosting a Leadership Retreat this week and just happened to see a flyer at the Down to Earth grocery store the other day featuring Nick, so I wanted to come out and see another speaker perform his craft and learn more of his story about the challenges of being born without arms or legs."

The line continued to be stagnant with no one moving an inch forward toward the entrance. Kaika replied, "What is a leadership guru?"

John replied, "I help people and organizations maximize their leadership potential so they can get better results in both work and life." Kaika asked, "Does being selected captain of your baseball team count as being a leader?"

John replied, "Yes, of course; being selected captain of your team is quite an impressive recognition, but it also comes with great responsibilities. You should be very proud and take this role seriously."

Kaika replied, "How then can I become a better leader and get my teammates to follow me? What advice can you give me on the subject of leadership?" John replied, "My best advice for becoming a great leader is to understand and live by this mantra:

> **"The key to becoming an effective leader is not to focus on making other people follow, but on making yourself the kind of person they *want* to follow."**

Kaika responded, "I am working very hard this summer on being a better person, and on starting a business to raise money for my baseball team's trip to California. So I will use your advice in leading our team."

Just as Kaika finished his sentence, everyone in the line quickly ran over to the yard area beside the gymnasium where it appeared Nick was addressing the eager audience.

As a result, Kaika did not get a chance to thank John properly or say goodbye to him. However, John's wisdom was priceless, and Kaika was for sure going to write that quote in his journal.

Furthermore, John's advice must have hit home because that night when Kaika went to bed he tossed and turned and couldn't sleep.

So he got out of bed and found a book on the family bookshelf about the "leadership" styles of all the past United States' Presidents.

Not only did he read most of the book, but he quickly decided that John F. Kennedy was his favorite president because he was such a passionate and memorable speaker. He was also impressed that JFK was one of the youngest presidents ever elected into office.

He was so intrigued that he wondered whether many of the U.S. Presidents had been elected as captains of their baseball teams when they were kids.

EXERCISE:

What are five things you can do to grow as a person and become a better leader so you will encourage more people to *want* to follow you?

1._____

2._____

3._____

4._____

5._____

Chapter 12

REFUSING TO GIVE UP

As it turned out, Nick, who was scheduled to speak that night in The War Memorial Gymnasium from 7-8 p.m. to a jam-packed audience, was disappointed to learn that the gymnasium held only 2,500 people, leaving another 1,000 people stuck waiting outside in the parking lot in line, hoping to get in to hear him speak.

Around 6 p.m., Nick pulled up outside in his wheelchair. He had no arms and legs so he controlled the wheelchair by a joystick, maneuvering it with his tiny foot that extended from his left hip. On the back of his wheelchair, he had a sticker from the automobile manufacturer "BMW."

Nick suddenly yelled out to the crowd: "I want to thank all of you for coming, but I am sorry to say we only have 2,500 seats inside, and that leaves about 1,000 of you out here unable to get in. I am supposed to start speaking inside the gym in an hour, and unfortunately, none of you are going to be able to come in to be seated."

Nick continued: "Therefore, if it is okay with all of you, you are welcome to come sit in the grassy area, and within five minutes or so, I will give the exact same speech out here in the grass that I am going to give inside in an hour. So everyone come have a seat in front of me here in the grass and I will begin in about five minutes."

Kaika was in awe of what he was witnessing since he had never before seen a human being without arms or legs. He was also so very impressed that Nick did not send everyone home, but rather was willing to do a second speech (prior to his scheduled speech), just to ensure that no one would go home disappointed.

Kaika wanted to go meet Nick, so he climbed over the fence just as fast as he could and ran right up to meet him while everyone was getting seated. Kaika then said, "Hello, Mister. My name is Kaika and I am very excited to hear you speak.

"I want to know: How have you managed to live your life with no arms and no legs? Perhaps there have been times when you wanted to quit, and yet you obviously continued your journey. I am going through a tough time now and wondered if you could share some insights with me?"

Nick responded, "While, yes, of course, there have been many times I have wanted to quit and give up, I have persevered instead. Why do you ask about giving up, Kaika?"

Kaika responded, "I am selling hand-carved makau fishhook necklaces in an effort to raise money for my baseball team's trip to California. But I have worked several days in the hot sun in an effort to make these sales, and to date, only one person, named Les, has purchased a necklace from me."

"I am very discouraged and starting to think that my plan will not work. As a result, I am completely unsure what to do next. Most of my friends are hanging out at the beach all day enjoying their summer vacations while I am stuck in the hot sun working all day, and I have only made one sale."

Nick responded, "Growing up and looking the way I do, many times I thought God did not like me so I considered suicide! However, I realized that I was put here on earth to make a difference, just as you are, Kaika. My best advice that I can give you is this:

"Sometimes you may feel like you are about to realize your goal only to fall short. That is no reason to quit. Defeat happens only to those who refuse to try again."

Kaika thanked Nick for his advice. Then the conversation abruptly ended as Nick was getting ready to give his speech. Kaika stood to the side of Nick in his wheelchair, leaning up against the rusty fence, and was eager to soak up all the great advice Nick was about to offer.

Nick started his speech by saying, "My name is Nick and I am from Australia, but now I live in California. As you can see, I was born with no arms and no legs. What you cannot see is that my condition has not kept me from enjoying many great adventures, a fulfilling and meaningful career, and a loving relationship...."

Kaika stood there, leaning up against the fence at the front of the audience in awe as Nick spoke with passion from his heart at the top of his lungs to a crowd of at least 1,000 people, now sitting in front of him on the lawn and listening attentively. Nick continued with his speech and said, "Putting faith in action is about believing and achieving. It is about having faith in yourself, your talents, your purpose, and most of all, in God's love and His divine plan for your life...."

Kaika didn't remember much more than that from Nick's speech, but his personal conversation with Nick left him more inspired than ever. Kaika was so inspired at what had just happened that he stopped at the big book display table where there was a line of people buying books. This display was located just outside the back entrance to the War Memorial Coliseum. Kaika purchased a copy of Nick's book, titled *Unstoppable*. He then jumped on his bike and headed for home as the sun set behind the West Maui Mountains in the Iao Valley. Kaika was now more determined than ever to sell his hand-carved makaus the very next day under the banyan tree.

EXERCISE:

List three reasons why you will never give up on your journey to becoming a successful entrepreneur.

1._____

2._____

3._____

Chapter 13

PROTECTING THE FAMILY

Kaika continued to go to the swap meet and banyan tree every Saturday, Sunday, and Monday. He would sit out in the hot sun and sell his makau fishhook necklaces. As a result of his newfound determination and "never quit" mentality, he quickly sold another $200 worth of hand-carved makaus and almost earned his way on the baseball trip that was fast approaching. However, now that he was soon to achieve his goal, he wanted to continue selling so he could help his mother buy groceries.

Sometimes, Leilani, who was fast becoming Kaika's best friend and girlfriend, would come with him when he sold his makau fishhook necklaces. But sometimes she didn't because she didn't like being in the hot sun. Kaika noticed that he always sold more necklaces whenever Leilani was with him, so naturally he wanted her with him as much as possible. Plus their conversations kept them both entertained between customers.

On this particular Monday evening, Kaika looked up and noticed a couple sitting on the park bench near the banyan tree eating Baskin-Robbins ice cream. He approached the couple and asked, "Would you like to buy a necklace?"

The man said, "Sure, why not? I love supporting young entrepreneurs; in fact, my son, Patrick, is a business owner." While Kaika was wrapping the makau necklace, he asked the man, "What is your name? What do you do for a living? And where are you from?" The man replied, "My name is Jack, and this is my lovely wife, Lois. I am a retired school-teacher and golf coach from Michigan."

Jack then shared with Kaika that they had been visiting for a few days and had noticed that sometimes Kaika had a helper and other times he didn't. "Is she your sister?" Jack asked. "No," Kaika replied. "She is my neighbor and good friend, but one day I would like her to be my wife, but don't tell her that!"

Jack said, "Don't worry; your secret is safe with me. I am not a relationship expert, but I have been married to my wife Lois for more than fifty years and I have learned many things. Let me just share this wisdom with you before we need to get back to the cruise ship:

"Family is the most important thing in the world. You must fight to protect your family and keep it together, always!"

Kaika thanked Jack for his advice. Then Jack and Lois took their makau fishhook necklace and ice cream cones and headed back to the cruise ship as it was getting ready to depart the harbor.

EXERCISE:

List five actions you can take immediately to protect your family further and keep it together always.

1._____

2._____

3._____

4._____

5._____

- Chapter 14 -

PLAYING WHEN HURT

The next morning, remembering Jack's advice about family being the most important thing in the world, Kaika quickly accepted an invitation to go boogie boarding at Makena Beach with Leilani and her family. There was a south swell that was coming in and the waves were expected to be quite high. The shore break at Makena is quite steep, making it a bad angle to get swept up in by the waves. Many amateurs had broken their necks on this beach due to the shore break. Leilani and Kaika had been going there for years, though, so they were not worried.

On this particular day, the waves were even bigger than anticipated at 8-10 feet, so Kaika and Leilani were a bit concerned, but they dove into the water anyway. After about thirty minutes of hard boogie boarding, a big wave caught Kaika by surprise and slammed him very hard onto the sandy beach at the shore break. Kaika found himself experiencing intense pain in his side. He was done for the day.

Leilani's mom felt bad for Kaika so she surprised both Kaika and Leilani by stopping in Kihei at their favorite restaurant: Taqueria Cruz.

This was a big treat for both of them because Taqueria Cruz is known throughout the Pacific for having the best Mexican food. Kaika got his favorite, a big fat juicy burrito, and Leilani got her favorite, a chimichanga, and they split an order of tortilla chips. They especially enjoyed the live music. Even though his ribs hurt, Kaika fell a little deeper in love with Leilani that night as a result of this special dinner.

Kaika was not able to sleep much that night due to his sore ribs so his mother took him to the doctor's office the next day.

The x-ray showed that he had broken two ribs. Kaika was very concerned about this since the big baseball tournament in California was only a few weeks away.

That evening, Kaika showed up for baseball practice to tell Coach Bill about his injury.

Coach Bill was kind of "old school" and pushed his players to the very edges of their mental limits, making them become even stronger athletes and more disciplined young men.

When Coach Bill saw Kaika at practice with an Ace bandage wrapped around his midsection, he said, "Okay, Kaika; what did you do now?"

Kaika replied, "I broke two of my ribs boogie boarding at Makena Beach and the doctor said I should rest up for 2-3 weeks." Coach Bill replied, "But our tournament is in two weeks, so hopefully, you will be ready by then. You are our only left-handed pitcher and we also need you at first base."

Coach Bill also had coached Kaika in football for years, so they had a very strong relationship, almost like that of a father and son. Kaika knew Coach Bill admired him because Coach Bill pushed him harder than any of the other players on his football team.

Kaika had learned many lessons about life from playing football for Coach Bill, including the importance of determination, perseverance, and working harder than everyone else in order to achieve your goals.

Kaika replied with a smile and said, "No need to worry, Coach Bill. I promise I will be ready to play in the tournament. But just in case I am aching and moaning about the pain, tell me again what you have been telling us for years during football season."

Coach Bill cracked up laughing (since they constantly joked with each other), smiled, and said:

> **"You have to play when you are hurt**
> **if you want to win. Sooner or later,**
> **you will learn that all of those who**
> **achieved tremendous feats in life,**
> **at one time or another,**
> **'played hurt.'"**

Kaika remembered this saying from football season, smiled, and said, "Don't worry, Coach. I will be ready for the tournament and promise that I will not go boogie boarding again until after the California trip." This conversation again reminded Kaika that football was his favorite sport.

Kaika then watched the practice from the bleachers, but he was determined to come back and join the team as soon as possible.

As he watched the practice, Kaika realized that in the absence of his father, who was stationed overseas in the military, he was really lucky to have someone like Coach Bill in his life whom he could talk to about anything. Kaika really felt that this friendship with his coach would last a lifetime.

EXERCISE:

What are five nagging health issues you have in your life that are plaguing you and slowing you down? I challenge you to identify them and then squarely address each one (for example: being overweight, a bad back, knee problems, etc.).

1._____

2._____

3._____

4._____

5._____

- *Chapter 15* -

EXPECTING TO WIN

As it turned out, Coach Bill had asked Kaika's mother several weeks earlier whether he could lend their family the amount needed to bring Kaika to California to play in the baseball tournament.

Kaika's mother agreed to accept the loan for the trip under one condition—that Kaika would have to repay his coach in full for the loan since she could not afford to repay the loan with her income from the restaurant.

Kaika agreed to repay the loan and felt good about it since he had already sold many of his hand-carved makaus, but he asked Coach Bill whether he could have twelve months to do so. His coach agreed to the terms. (Coach Bill, however, really felt the loan was more like a scholarship or a gift. Never in a million years did he think a sixth grader could earn and pay $200 back for the loan.)

Kaika continued to sell his makaus even though he was "playing hurt" (at work). Kaika's ribs were still sore, but he was ready to play in the tournament to lead his teammates on as captain. The team got to the Maui airport early and checked in together as a group. They went through security and were soon ready for early boarding. They all felt very special for getting to board their plane bound for California ten minutes earlier than the other passengers.

Kaika led his teammates down the Jetway and into the plane. They all sat next to each other in the very back of the plane. Then, to their surprise, one of the plane's pilots came back to join them for a bit.

Kaika looked up at him and said, "Are you the captain or the co-captain of this plane?" Surprised by this question, the man replied, "My name is Captain Rob and I will be flying you to your destination in California today. I promise to get you there safely. Tell me about the tournament your team is playing in."

Kaika replied, "It is a round-robin tournament where you play ten games in seven days, and the winner is the team that has the best record after everyone plays each other. Did you ever play baseball? Did you ever know anyone who played in the pros?"

Rob replied, "Well, my brother Brad actually played professional football in the NFL for the New York Giants. Also, I played both baseball and football for many years, so if you are interested, I can share with you what it takes to develop the mind of a world champion."

Kaika replied, "Of course, Captain Rob. We are competing against the best teams from Northern California, Southern California, Washington, Oregon, and Nevada so we need all the help we can get!"

Captain Rob replied, "I used to be an athlete, and I also coached high school football and basketball for years. I learned that anyone who plays sports and learns about teamwork, discipline, perseverance, and never giving up has an advantage both in life and business by transferring that discipline for sports into dedication to both academics and his or her career.

I used to tell my players this message, and they would apply it as part of their pre-game preparation and became champions year after year. Therefore, the best advice I can offer you as you get prepared for each game is:

"The difference between winners and losers is that winners show up expecting to win, while losers show up hoping to win!"

Captain Rob continued, "All right, guys; that is all I've got for you. I challenge you to develop the 'expectation for winning' in each and every game you play, and then you will be successful! I need to get back up in the cockpit now to perform my pre-flight checklist. Good luck to you guys!"

Kaika replied, "Thank you, Captain Rob!" It was then and there that Kaika realized the wisdom in what Coach Bill had taught them in football when he made the connection between your mind, athletics, and business. It all seemed to be inter-related since sports was a natural apprenticeship to succeeding later in business.

Since they traveled on a red-eye flight, Kaika's teammates slept most of the way. Kaika, however, did not sleep that well since his ribs were still sore and the plane's seats were not as comfortable as his bed. Thankfully, though, Kaika did put his headphones on and watched two movies on the screens that were lowered from the ceiling in transit while his teammates slept.

EXERCISE:

What are five challenges / tournaments / compe-
titions in which you need to develop the "expectation to win" and in which you MUST win in order
to attain your goals?

1._____

2._____

3._____

4._____

5._____

Chapter 16

BECOMING A CHAMPION

As soon as the team landed and got checked into the hotel, Kaika called a "players-only" meeting. He gathered his teammates and encouraged them to have fun during this week, but also to take the games seriously. He encouraged them at sixty-minutes prior to the first pitch to quit goofing around and focus on the game ahead. He challenged them to make the decision to pre-determine a victorious outcome in advance of each game (just as Captain Rob had described). He challenged them to create the "expectation to win" and never give up, regardless of the score.

Kaika's speech was effective. Sore ribs and all, he led his team as captain to a record of 9-1, becoming co-champions. But since the other team that they tied with scored more runs against common opponents, Kaika's team would not go on to the next round of the tournament. The other team would go play in Pennsylvania and Kaika's team would return to Hawai`i.

Kaika had a great experience, met lots of new people, and got to travel outside of Hawai`i for the very first time in his life. Coach Bill and most of his teammates felt that Captain Rob's speech on the plane and his advice to develop the "expectation to win" was partly responsible for their team's success. Also, everyone loved playing for Coach Bill since he made it so much fun while at the same time developing each player into a solid young man.

However, while on this trip, before and after each of his games, Kaika could not stop thinking about getting back home to Maui so he could see Leilani again and make more money selling his makaus at the swap meet and under the banyan tree. Kaika really wanted to transfer some of the lessons he learned in sports to his life in business selling his hand-carved necklaces to tourists.

It seemed as if Kaika was more excited about selling his product than he was about baseball. He really enjoyed becoming an entrepreneur. Despite winning, inside his heart, Kaika realized at this tournament that his future was in business and not in baseball. Because of his love for football and the impact that Coach Bill had on his life, he had started to dream of one day playing pro football. But now, he became fascinated with the term entrepreneur. He studied the pronunciation of it, spelling of it, and its definition (which he learned from one mentor):

Entrepreneur: A person who overcomes risk by making his or her own money by selling a product or service in volume to others in need.

As a result of this trip and his experience that summer selling his creations, Kaika decided that not only was he going to go to college, but he was going to study business and graduate from college. This was a significant decision for him to make since no one before him in his family had ever graduated from college.

EXERCISE:

What are five habits that you need to implement in your life to develop a world-champion mindset?

1._____

2._____

3._____

4._____

5._____

Chapter 17

CREATING MULTIPLE STREAMS OF INCOME

Upon returning from California, Kaika carved another dozen makaus and then dashed off to the banyan tree on his bike to set up his shop. He was eager to get back to work.

The first tourist off the cruise ship that day was an older man with long hair, and he spoke with an English accent. He approached Kaika and said, "Here is $100. I will buy four makau fishhook necklaces." Kaika smiled, took his money, and said, "Thank you!" He then said to the tourist, "You have an interesting accent, Mister! What is your name and where are you from?" The older man smiled and said, "My name is Richard and I live on my own island named Necker Island. It is in the British Virgin Islands. However, I am originally from London, England."

Kaika immediately asked, "What do you do for a living that allows you to afford your own island and travel so far from home?" Richard replied, "I am a business owner just like you, except I actually own 350 businesses, including a record label and an airline." Kaika replied, "Why do you own so many businesses?" Richard said, "Son, let me share a lesson with you that my mentor taught me many years ago: Don't put all your eggs in one basket! The key to success in business and life is to develop multiple streams of income and:

"There is no greater thing you can do with your life than follow your passions—in a way that serves the world and you."

Richard continued, "You should look at your talents and see whether you can create additional products you can sell to these tourists. If you double the amount of inventory you offer, you can also double the amount of profits you make."

Kaika thanked Richard for his advice, and that night, he rode his bike straight home with the idea of selling bracelets as well.

He took the same hemp string he used for the necklaces and went to talk to his grandmother. He asked her whether he could use her beads in the art drawer to place on the bracelets and she agreed.

By the next week, Kaika was able to sell both makau fishhook necklaces and beaded bracelets outside the swap meet and also under the banyan tree. By the time the summer was half over, Kaika had surpassed $2,000 in sales since he spent his weekdays carving necklaces and making bracelets. He now had more than enough money to pay back Coach Bill for the trip to California. Coach Bill reluctantly accepted the $200 to repay the loan (not because he needed the money but rather to help Kaika realize the importance of repaying your debts).

EXERCISE:

List five different streams of income that you can develop for your family (for example, day job income, writing a book, speaking, coaching, consulting, real estate, network marketing, selling on eBay / Craigslist, buying and selling cars, or other business opportunities):

1._____

2._____

3._____

4._____

5._____

Chapter 18

TAKING ACTION

The following Saturday morning, Kaika was set up at seven o'clock just outside the swap meet's entrance. At 8:30, a man and his wife stopped to ask him about his venture. The man said, "My name is Patrick, and I am an author, speaker, and publishing coach, so I just wanted to come over and congratulate you on building your own business! Most importantly, I am a father and I have been encouraging my two boys each to create his own business. This is why I was attracted to your sales stand."

Kaika was very proud to hear these words. With a smile, he replied, "Thank you, Patrick!" Then Patrick asked, "What are your dreams and goals? What do you want to do when you grow up? Have you ever written out your goals?" Kaika said, "When I grow up, I want to play professional football, then own a pro sports team and a cruise line so I can travel all over the world and see the places where all my clients I have met during the summer come from. The only problem is I have no idea how to achieve such a goal and what actions I should take between now and then!"

Patrick replied, "You don't need to know the how! All you have to do is believe in your visions and sooner or later, the 'HOW' will show up in your life. The key to achieving your dreams is to *take action* and live by this mantra:

"DREAM the impossible.
PLAN for success.
EXECUTE your visions.
SOAR in life."

Patrick continued, "Kaika, the important thing to remember is that first you need to dream. Next, you need to come up with a game plan for how you will achieve your dreams. Then, you will need to *take action* and *execute* your goals. Action equals results! Massive action equals massive results.

When you dream, plan, and execute, you will ultimately create your own destiny and soar in life. In doing so, you will attain a great balance between family, faith, wealth, and health! Remember this forever, Kaika. You are the one who decides the fate of your life as destiny occurs by 'choice' not by 'chance.'"

"One last thing," Patrick said. "My father had me fill out my first goal sheets when I was in the eighth grade. As a result, I earned my college degree and became an author, speaker, publishing coach, and an entrepreneur.

I successfully raised two amazing boys I am so proud of, and I even was able to move to Maui, all as a result of my father having me fill out the goal sheets. If you, too, want to take charge of your life, become the captain of your ship, and the creator of your destiny, I encourage you to do the same.

In fact, you can go to my website once you get home and print out your free goal sheets to complete. Just visit the website:

www.CreateYourOwnDestiny.com

Click on 'Free Stuff' on the Navigation Bar to print out your free goal sheets."

Patrick proceeded to buy a makau fishhook for himself and a bracelet for his beautiful wife, Nicole. Kaika thanked them and proceeded to sell another set to the next couple waiting in line behind them.

Later that evening, Kaika wrote out the following ten "TO DO" goals on his goal sheet and looked at it regularly for many years to come:

1. Graduate from college

2. Marry Leilani

3. Play professional football and buy a pro sports team

4. Purchase a cruise line

5. Become a lifelong entrepreneur

6. Live in Maui

7. Have two sons and one daughter

8. Mentor youth of today to become leaders of tomorrow

9. Write a best-selling book

10. Become a professional speaker

EXERCISE:

What are five actions you need to take, ideas to pursue, or achievements to earn for you to create your own destiny?

1._____

2._____

3._____

4._____

5._____

Chapter 19

VALUING EDUCATION

The next day under the banyan tree, Kaika was approached by an older, slightly balding man who started talking to him and asked him questions about his schooling.

Kaika said, "Before I answer all your questions about my schooling and grade level, tell me a bit about yourself." The man said, "My name is Jim and I am a professional speaker. I have worked in the direct sales and network marketing industries as a home-based business trainer for many years. Now tell me what grade you are in. Do you understand the power of a solid education? Are you excited that one day you will graduate and leave school?"

Kaika replied, "I just finished the sixth grade, and I am starting in the seventh in September. I have not really thought much about my life after school, other than one day I want to own a cruise line! What advice can you give me about the importance of a good education?"

Jim replied, "A good education is one of the most important investments you can make in your life. However, most people believe that education lasts only through the twelfth grade (or perhaps through college). My belief on this subject matter is:

"Formal education will make you a living; self-education will make you a fortune!"

"So I challenge you never to stop learning after graduation; rather, focus on continuous learning as a way of life. Challenge yourself to learn for a lifetime despite how old you eventually become. And reading is one of the best ways to learn. After all, *readers are leaders*!"

Kaika was awestruck by this statement. So much so that Kaika decided then and there that he would go to the library in his free time and read the biographies of successful entrepreneurs in hopes he could learn even more ways to succeed in business.

Jim then purchased three makaus for $75 and went on his way.

Kaika continued to collect and write all these quotes he was learning throughout the summer in his journal. However, he was completely unaware who these people really were and why none of them ever offered up his or her last name. He thought that maybe they were famous, yet humble, and did not want to draw attention to themselves.

EXERCISE:

What are five ways in which you can improve or grow your "self-education" (for example, reading books, attending seminars, etc.)?

1._____

2._____

3._____

4._____

5._____

- Chapter 20 -

BEING BOLD

Later that day, Kaika was approached by an older man. This man looked at Kaika's necklaces and bracelets with an approving smile and said, "Tell me more about your business!"

Kaika replied, "My name is Kaika and I am selling Hawaiian makau fishhook necklaces and bracelets. I started so I could afford to go with my baseball team to play in a tournament in California. Coach Bill gave me a $200 loan for the trip, but now I have sold enough and I repaid him, but I am continuing to sell anyway as a way to contribute to my family."

Then because Kaika was beginning to appreciate the wisdom he was gaining from all his clients, he asked the man, "What is your name, and what advice can you give a young entrepreneur such as myself?"

The man replied, "My name is Brian, and I am the author of more than forty books. I am originally from Vancouver in British Columbia, Canada. But

I have resided in Southern California for several years. The best advice I can give you to succeed in business is:

**"Act boldly,
and unseen forces
will come to your aid!"**

"Additionally, I would advise you to learn to 'Go for the No's.' If you want to earn one million dollars per year, all you need to do is to wake up early each morning and get ten in your face, smack-down rejections by 9 a.m. each day. When you successfully get this many rejections by 9 a.m. each day, I promise you, you will become a millionaire! Business is a numbers game. The more sales presentations you give, the greater the odds of bringing on more customers."

Kaika thanked him for this advice and then smiled when the man bought two makau fishhook necklaces and one bracelet. Before he returned to the cruise ship, Brian wished Kaika good luck in his summer business venture.

As a result of Brian's advice, Kaika realized that every "No" in sales can be a good thing as it increases the odds of getting a "Yes" from the next prospect.

EXERCISE:

What are five personal attributes you can develop that will make you more bold in business and life (example: learning to love prospecting in your business, asking for the business, asking for referrals, etc.)?

1._____

2._____

3._____

4._____

5._____

- Chapter 21 -

SAVING MONEY

Thirty minutes later, a very sharply dressed woman with a smile on her face approached the banyan tree. Looking intrigued by Kaika's sales stand, she asked, "How are your sales coming along? Are you making lots of money? What are you doing with your income? How much of your profits are you saving for the future?"

Kaika was impressed by this woman's strong interest in what he was doing. He excitedly replied, "I would love to answer all your questions, but first tell me your name and a bit about yourself?"

The woman responded, "My name is Suze, and I started as a waitress before buying my own restaurant. Now I am a financial advisor and TV show host. I am originally from Chicago, but now I split my time between three homes in San Francisco, New York, and Florida." Kaika said, "It must be nice to own three homes; many people in Hawai`i can barely afford one. But to answer your question, I have sold $3,500 worth of necklaces and bracelets. As a result, I paid off my baseball coach's $200 loan, leaving me $3,300 to buy more hemp string and help my mother with our groceries."

Suze said, "That is wonderful that you have cleared your debt and provided assistance to your mother! But what are you going to do with the rest of your money? What percentage of your sales are you planning on saving?"

Kaika replied, "I don't know. I guess I have not really thought about what to do with the rest of this money or how much I should save." Suze said, "If you are open to my advice, I would say that the key to achieving your money goals is:

**"Make a decision to keep some of
all the money you earn!"**

Suze then said, "By 'keeping,' I am referring to the best habit you can develop which is 'saving' your money."

Kaika decided then and there that he would not go out to the Queen Ka'ahumanu Mall and buy things with his profits, but rather save all of his profits after he helped his mother buy groceries.

EXERCISE:

What are five things you can do immediately to your family budget to save more money both in terms of your expenses and in saving more of your income?

1._____

2._____

3._____

4._____

5._____

- *Chapter 22* -

LIVING WITH PASSION

After making sales to Brian and Suze, Kaika was really happy and felt a power inside him as he learned about being bold. Another strength he felt was the peace of mind it gave him to know that he was saving his money instead of wasting it. He was very happy to be able to assist his mother with other expenses when she needed help.

He packed up his crate, his unsold makau necklaces, and his white towel and headed home with a boost of confidence in his step, eager to continue to grow and learn. As he headed up the road toward Wailuku, he noticed that the parking lot at U. Hawai`i Maui Campus was packed with cars.

Normally in the evening, there were no cars there. This change caught his attention, so instead of going home, he parked and locked his bike, walked across the large grassy area, and went up to the auditorium.

He peeked inside and saw at least 500-750 people watching a speaker talk.

There was a guy at the door with a nametag on that read "Tom." He whispered to Kaika that he was welcome to come in as long as he kept quiet. Kaika replied to this stranger, "Who is the guy on the stage speaking, and what is the event that has attracted so many people?"

Tom replied, "It is Steve from California who is presenting on campus at our technology and computer forum. His talk is almost finished, but come on in and sit here in the back row."

Without hesitation, Kaika entered and took a seat. He was immediately drawn into the amazing images on the big screen. Kaika saw many images that he had never seen before, and he felt a passion and conviction in Steve's voice that very few adults will ever have in a lifetime. Kaika's jaw dropped, and he was immediately just sucked into the voice, the passion, the conviction, the ability to communicate with images, and that this speaker was able to hold the audience in the palm of his hand.

Steve went on to say, "It is so important to follow your passions, live your life on your terms, demand more from yourself, and then create a future for yourself that you craft on your terms."

When the final slide was displayed, it too caught Kaika's eye so he asked Tom, "Can I borrow a pen and a piece of paper, so I can jot down this quote?" Tom replied, handing the items to him, "Sure, here you go."

As Steve finished his speech, he read these words that literally spoke right to Kaika's heart:

"Your time is limited, so don't waste it living someone else's life. Don't be trapped by dogma—which is living with the results of other people's thinking. Don't let the noise of others' opinions drown out your inner voice. And most important, have the courage to follow your heart and intuition."

With these words, all in the audience gave Steve a standing ovation, which lasted for several minutes. Then many of the people in the audience swarmed the stage to meet this Steve guy. Kaika too wanted to meet him and shake his hand because he sensed that Steve would one day become a very influential person. However, it was getting late and Kaika knew his mother would worry about him if he didn't get home before dark.

So Kaika folded up his sheet of paper with Steve's quote handwritten on it, placed it in his pocket, and then headed out the door. He jumped on his bike and pedaled quickly to get home before dark.

Kaika was so impressed with Steve's presentation that on his bike ride on the way home, he decided that at the end of the summer, he would take some of his earnings and buy himself a laptop computer.

This was a big decision in Kaika's mind since not a single one of his friends who was going into the seventh grade owned his own laptop computer.

Kaika was very proud to become the first of his friends to make such a purchase. More so, he was proud to be learning the importance of investing in yourself if you are to succeed in school, life, and business. Kaika was convinced that a new laptop computer would serve him well as an entrepreneur.

EXERCISE:

Knowing that your time on earth is limited and understanding the importance of living out your own life, what are five of your biggest passions that you love to do, for yourself, in your free time? When you are not a parent, a husband, a wife, a son, or a daughter, what are five of your greatest passions that you would like to put into action?

1._____

2._____

3._____

4._____

5._____

Chapter 23

SERVING OTHERS

Two weekends later, the summer was coming to an end, and Kaika remembered that he needed to write his two-page paper to turn into his seventh grade teacher on the first day of school. By this time, Kaika's personal journal was full of quotes and entrepreneurial advice. Throughout the summer, he had jotted down in his journal every bit of wisdom and advice from his many clients from all over the world. They had each provided valuable wisdom and advice for a new business owner.

That morning, an older fellow and his redheaded wife walked up to Kaika. The man said, in a funny Southern accent, "Why, good morning, young fellow. What are you selling?"

Kaika confidently replied, "Nothing less than the finest hand-carved Hawaiian jewelry in all the mighty Pacific. You won't find another set of jewelry anywhere in the world as nice and polished as this set! How many sets are you going to take home today for your family and friends?"

Clearly, as Kaika had sold more and more throughout the summer, his confidence and sales skills had improved tremendously.

The man smiled, said it was a pleasure to meet a young entrepreneur, and told Kaika his name was Zig. Then Zig said, "You remind me of how I became the number one door-to-door salesman of cookware in all of the South!" Kaika replied, "Please do share how you became the number one salesman in your company." Zig excitedly replied in his Yazoo City, Mississippi, accent, "The key to my success in life is the same key that will make you successful. It is to understand this principle and apply it to your every relationship for the rest of your life:

"You can have everything in life you want if you help enough other people get what they want!"

Kaika smiled because he understood the value of this advice. Zig then bought out the remainder of Kaika's inventory. This kind of sale had never happened before, so he worked hard every evening all the next week carving new inventory to prepare for the last weekend before school started again.

EXERCISE:

Take an inventory of your talents and passions, and now list five ways you can bring more value to the marketplace and be of even more service to people, organizations, or non-profits in your community:

1._____

2._____

3._____

4._____

5._____

- Chapter 24 -

GIVING TO THOSE IN NEED

It was Kaika's last weekend of selling before he would write his two-page paper and head back to school to start the seventh grade on Monday. After a busy week of carving, Kaika eagerly walked back to the swap meet on Saturday morning with hopes of selling out his inventory. He walked because his bike had a flat tire.

As he walked down the hill from Wailuku heading to the swap meet in Kahului, he noticed an older woman carrying two very heavy bags of groceries.

Her back was slouched over from carrying the heavy bags. This alarmed Kaika because she was obviously too old and too frail to be carrying so much weight.

Upon seeing her, Kaika rushed up to this woman and said, "My name is Kaika and I am wondering if I can help you carry these groceries?" The elderly woman replied, "And my name is Teresa, and yes, of course, I would be thrilled if you can help me."

Kaika then moved aside his inventory of makau necklaces and bracelets and placed both bags of groceries inside the light blue milk crate. As he carried the groceries and began to walk with her, Kaika asked, "Where did you get these groceries, and where are you going with them? Also where are you from?"

Teresa replied, "I live in a faraway place on the other side of the world. My organization told me I was working too hard and needed to get some rest. So they sent me here on vacation.

Upon arrival, I read in *The Maui News* that the Maui Food Bank was severely low on food. So instead of staying at my hotel and relaxing beside the pool, I decided to walk to the grocery store to buy some food and then hand-deliver it to the Maui Food Bank."

Kaika replied, "Well, then let's walk together and deliver these groceries. I would like to help the Maui Food Bank out." They then both walked about six blocks in the other direction from the swap meet.

On their walk, Kaika asked Teresa, "But why on your vacation are you spending your time doing this instead of enjoying the pool?" Teresa then replied with a most amazing answer—it completely caught Kaika off-guard and meant so much to him that her words were forever imprinted on his mind. Teresa said:

**"Not all of us can do great things.
But we can do small things
with great love.
If you can't feed a hundred people,
feed just one."**

This quote impacted Kaika so much that when he got to the Maui Food Bank with Teresa, he pulled out $50 from his business money bag (which was given to him by the bank teller at Bank of Hawaii) and gave it as a donation to the Maui Food Bank to purchase more groceries.

This was a big thing for Kaika to do since he had never even given away $5 before. He hugged Teresa and she thanked him for his help in carrying the groceries.

With a smile, he headed back toward the swap meet, feeling that he had just helped some people in need on Maui to be fed. His heart was warm and he was grateful for this experience.

Never in Kaika's life had he ever felt such a warm joy and peace radiating from his heart, which resulted from his good deeds of carrying the groceries and giving of his own money.

At this moment, he realized he had just given away the full amount of the $50 tip that Les had given him, and he understood how important it is to move money in a local economy (especially to serve those who need it).

As a result of this experience, Kaika decided then and there, no matter how successful he ever became in life, he would always give of both his time and money to lend a hand to serve those in need.

He decided that once school started up again at the end of August, he would wake up early on Saturday mornings, ride his bike down to the Maui Food Bank, and volunteer his time to help feed the less fortunate ones in his community.

He hoped by supporting such a worthwhile cause that he could help make a difference in other people's lives. Kaika could think of no better way to achieve this goal than to volunteer and feed the hungry in his local community. As a result, he was inspired to start a food drive at school.

EXERCISE:

List five organizations in your community that give of their time, energy, and money to support those in need. Now circle the one that you feel most drawn to assist. Finally, as soon as you are done reading this book, call that organization and schedule an appointment to learn how you can give of your time to assist it in its mission.

1._____

2._____

3._____

4. _____

5. _____

Chapter 25

COMMUNICATING
THE VISION

Because Kaika had helped Teresa with taking the groceries to the Maui Food Bank, he was late getting to the swap meet. However, he felt so good inside about his actions that he did not even care about being late.

While Kaika was sitting outside the swap meet entrance, a very old man approached and immediately bought one of Kaika's last makau necklaces. As Kaika collected the money and carefully wrapped the necklace in tissue, Kaika asked the old man, "Will you tell me your name, where you are from, and any advice you can give me since I need a few more entries for my school project that I am writing about what I learned this summer."

The wise old man replied, "My name is Clement and I worked in the insurance industry for many years in New York City. I am also a philanthropist. My mentor was a guy named Napoleon (who in turn was mentored by a guy named Andrew), and I learned many things from him. However, one of my best business secrets in life was to apply the following strategy toward the achievement of my goals:

"If you want something bad enough, tell everyone what you want to do, and someone will want to help you do it!"

When he heard this advice, Kaika got out his leather journal (that he had begun to bring with him to read when he had no customers) and jotted it down. Then he thanked the wise old man and watched him walk away with his cane assisting his every step.

Immediately, Kaika started thinking of the important mentors in his life with whom he felt comfortable sharing his dreams, goals, and visions...and Coach Bill was one of those he identified. He was eager to call Coach Bill and share the results of the summer.

He was also hopeful that soon his dad would return from being stationed overseas in the military, so he too could learn of his goals. Kaika was becoming eager to write his two-page paper and submit it to his new teacher at the end of the summer. He very much wanted to share his visions with others, and he thought his teacher would be interested.

EXERCISE:

Who are five someones (or somethings) who can show up in your life to help you achieve your dreams, goals, and visions? Maybe it is a coach, mentor, author, family member, or even your mother or father.

1._____

2._____

3._____

4._____

5._____

Chapter 26

LOVING ALL

After the last sale of the day, Kaika was completely out of inventory. He was so very happy to count his money and discover his total earnings for the summer, tips included, were $4,488. He had achieved all that by working only three days a week...and spending several weeknights carving his makau fishhooks and making his bracelets in his backyard.

Kaika then took out his journal and began to write in it. A minute later, a homeless man with a beard and long hair approached and asked Kaika, "What are you writing in your journal?" Kaika replied, "I have spent my summer interviewing some of the most successful business men and women in the world, seeking out their best advice to succeed in life. And, by the way, while I was conducting those interviews, I was also selling necklaces and bracelets. It seems what started as a summer business to earn money for a baseball trip has ended in a personal quest for knowledge from some of the most well-traveled and successful business people from all over the world."

As he spoke, Kaika was awestruck with the richness, warmth, and sparkle of the homeless man's bluish-green eyes. The dirty, ragged, long-haired man then asked Kaika, "Do you also want my advice to add to your journal?" Kaika replied with both suspicion and intrigue because this man did not seem to be a successful business owner. "Well, maybe, but who exactly are you? What advice can you offer me to succeed in life and business? I am not sure if I can actually learn anything from you."

The ragged man, who appeared to have no money and be homeless, replied, "My name is J.C. and I was born in a distant land, but I now live everywhere in the hearts of many. I may be one of the most controversial people you have met all summer. I am a philosopher and a salesman and some people believe in me (and follow my teachings as a result) while others do not, but many others confuse my message with religion and are quick to express their disbelief due to their misunderstanding of my message on love and forgiveness. This is okay, though, since I still love all of them. My best advice to you to include in your journal for living a peaceful and fulfilled life is:

"Love everyone,
and forgive all those who betray you!"

Kaika thanked J.C. for his advice and jotted it down as the homeless man walked away. Kaika felt that perhaps J.C.'s advice was the wisest and left the biggest impact of all the advice he had received all summer.

Due to the wisdom of J.C.'s advice, Kaika wondered whether J.C. could be the "someone" that Clement had just shared moments earlier. As a result, Kaika was now eager to get home, do some research on all these mentors, and write his two-page paper to turn it in to his new seventh grade teacher now that school was about to start.

EXERCISE:

Who are five people who have betrayed you that you need to forgive so you can move forward? Forgiveness is the best gift you can give to yourself.

1._____

2._____

3._____

4._____

5._____

Chapter 27

LEARNING FROM MENTORS

When Kaika returned home, the house was empty because both his mother and grandmother were working at their restaurant jobs. He decided to go in the backyard, lean up against the palm tree near the fence, and summarize the wisdom he had learned throughout this amazing summer. Here is the eight-page paper he wrote:

Lessons from the Summer after Sixth Grade

By: Ikaika Marks

(Iao Junior High – Grade 7)

Definition of an Entrepreneur:

A person who overcomes risk by making his or her own money by selling a product or service in volume to others in need.

Mega best-selling author
Mark Victor Hansen taught me...

**"You must A-S-K to G-E-T!
If you don't ask, you won't get."**

My sixth grade teacher
Mr. Brodi Goshi taught me...

"You become what you think about."

One of the best speakers and comedians
who has ever walked on this planet
Al Foxx taught me...

**"Focus on what you have,
not what you don't have!"**

Mr. Opportunity, Albert Mensah, taught me...

**"An opportunist is someone who
turns his obstacles and
adversities into new opportunities!**

Vision speaker and strategist
Larry Olsen taught me...

"You have no right to work on the 'how'
until you can taste, touch, smell, feel, hear,
emotionalize, and 'own the vision.'
The vision comes first and then you see 'how'
to accomplish your goals."

My grandfather taught me from a note he took
at a network marketing meeting...

"If you want what others have,
you must do what others have done,
and you will get what others have gotten!"

German Philosopher
Friedrich Nietzsche taught me...

"That which does not kill you, strengthens you!"

Inspirational fiction writer
Og Mandino taught me...

"Obstacles are necessary for success
because in selling,
as in all careers of importance,
victory only comes after many struggles
and countless defeats!"

The world's greatest professional speaker
Les Brown taught me...

"Never, under any circumstances, let someone
else's opinion of you determine your reality!"

Leadership guru John C. Maxwell taught me...

"The key to becoming an effective leader is not
to focus on making other people follow, but
on making yourself the kind of person they
want to follow."

Professional speaker, author, and evangelist
Nick Vujicic taught me...

"Sometimes you may feel like you are about to realize your goal only to fall short. That is no reason
to quit. Defeat happens only to those who refuse
to try again."

Schoolteacher, father, golf coach, and guitarist
Jack Snow taught me...

"Family is the most important thing in the world.
You must fight to protect your family and keep it
together, always!"

Football, wrestling, and baseball coach,
Bill McCarrick taught me...

"You have to play when you are hurt if you want to win. Sooner or later, you will learn that all of those who achieved tremendous feats in life, at one time or another, 'played hurt.'"

Airline captain, football coach, and father
Rob Van Pelt taught me...

"The difference between winners and losers is that winners show up expecting to win, while losers show up hoping to win!"

Billionaire Sir Richard Branson taught me...

"There is no greater thing you can do with your life than follow your passions—in a way that serves the world and you."

Publishing coach, international best-selling author, and professional speaker Patrick Snow taught me to write out my goals and to...

"DREAM the impossible. PLAN for success. EXECUTE your visions. SOAR in life."

Network marketing trainer, author, and speaker
Jim Rohn taught me...

**"Formal education will make you a living;
self-education will make you a fortune!"**

Corporate speaker and best-selling author
Brian Tracy taught me to go for the no's and to...

**"Act boldly
and unseen forces will come to your aid!"**

Financial wizard Suze Orman taught me...

**"Make a decision to keep some of all the
money you earn!"**

Founder of Apple Computers
Steve Jobs taught me...

**"Your time is limited, so don't waste it
living someone else's life. Don't be trapped
by dogma—which is living with the results of
other people's thinking. Don't let the noise
of others' opinions drown out your inner voice.
And most important, have the courage to
follow your heart and intuition."**

One of the world's best speakers
Zig Ziglar taught me...

**"You can have everything in life you want
if you help enough other people
get what they want!"**

Mother Teresa, who left one of the wealthiest
families in Albania and moved to India to
dedicate her life to serving those in
need, taught me...

**"Not all of us can do great things.
But we can do small things with great love.
If you can't feed a hundred people,
feed just one."**

Top insurance salesman W. Clement Stone,
who was mentored by Napoleon Hill
(who was mentored by Andrew Carnegie),
taught me...

**"If you want something bad enough,
tell everyone what you want to do,
and someone will
want to help you do it!"**

Lastly, J.C. is a perfect example of why we should never judge people based on the way they look, but rather on the kindness of their hearts and the goodness of their souls.

In all my research on the Internet trying to find my mentors' first and last names, I could not accurately identify J.C.

Perhaps it is because he was born in a faraway land, was homeless, or did not have a lot of money to afford a luxury cruise vacation.

J.C. remains a complete mystery to me! Even though I misjudged him because of the raggedness of his clothing, he still gave me the absolutely best advice of all my mentors when he taught me this important lesson:

**"Love everyone,
and forgive
all those
who betray you!"**

I am certainly glad that I saved my best interview for last. I have a feeling that J.C.'s advice will serve me well as I grow up and become an adult. One day, I hope to learn more about this man's real identity and his philosophy.

EXERCISE:

List your five greatest mentors in the lines below. Is J.C. one of those mentors? Why or why not?

1.＿＿＿＿＿＿＿＿＿＿＿＿＿＿＿＿＿＿＿

2.＿＿＿＿＿＿＿＿＿＿＿＿＿＿＿＿＿＿＿

3.＿＿＿＿＿＿＿＿＿＿＿＿＿＿＿＿＿＿＿

4.＿＿＿＿＿＿＿＿＿＿＿＿＿＿＿＿＿＿＿

5.＿＿＿＿＿＿＿＿＿＿＿＿＿＿＿＿＿＿＿

Chapter 28

LIVING LIFE ON PURPOSE

On the first day of seventh grade, Kaika turned in his eight-page paper. The next day, his teacher asked him to stay after class so he could talk to him. The teacher gave Kaika back his paper with an "A+" grade. Previous to this grade, Kaika never got more than a "B-" in any of his classes.

Then his teacher said to Kaika, "Not only are you ready for junior high, but you are ready for anything and everything that life presents to you! Most importantly, you have learned to 'fish for yourself' by earning your own money and creating your own business.

"Kaika, you have become an entrepreneur and are an inspiration to all of us who are still dependent on our employers. Now that you have created your own business, you can show others how to do it. You will never again in your life have to work for someone else because you know how to succeed by being self-employed. I wish I had learned this important skill early in my life as you have done. You are proof that the following quote from an unknown source is so true:

"Follow your dreams. Or you will spend the rest of your life working for someone who did."

Kaika was so inspired by his teacher's response that it gave him the extra boost of self-confidence he needed to run for class president (which he did), join Junior Achievement (which he did), join DECA (a school marketing organization), and FBLA (Future Business Leaders of America), both of which he did. Soon Kaika realized that his education was not just occurring in the classroom but in his ability to sell his visions to others, communicate with people of all ages, and to read books about personal growth and development outside of school hours.

All of these activities and what Kaika learned from them were setting him up to succeed in life as an entrepreneur who would enjoy freedom, free enterprise, and the ability completely to become the captain of his own ship, the creator of his own destiny, and allow him to get exactly what he wanted out of both life and work. He was more determined now than ever to write out his goals and pre-determine his destination in advance as Patrick had encouraged him. He did just this, and started on his amazing journey to freedom and success, achieving virtually all of his goals that he had written out on his goal sheets.

EXERCISE:

What are the five biggest challenges that are holding you back from achieving your dreams?

1._____

2._____

3._____

4._____

5._____

Chapter 29

ACHIEVING THE DREAM

Kaika eventually saved all of his money from all the many summers he sold his hand-carved makau necklaces and bracelets. In fact, he earned enough money to pay his entire way through college. After a football career-ending back injury, he graduated from college and moved to Seattle where he grew many more businesses and eventually earned enough money to purchase his own cruise line in Hawai`i.

Kaika moved back home to Maui and married his grade school sweetheart, Leilani. Together, they have two older boys and one girl. Kaika has become an author and professional speaker, and he volunteers his time in the community mentoring the youth of today to become the leaders of tomorrow. Kaika and Leilani purchased a minor-league Single-A pro baseball team and located it in Kahului, Maui, officially naming the team: Maui's Na Koa Ikaika (Hawaiian for "Powerful Warriors").

Their team played home games within walking distance of the swap meet parking lot (where Kaika had been first rejected for selling his makau hand-carved fishhook necklaces).

Currently, Kaika is in the process of putting an ownership group together to purchase an NFL football team and move it to Honolulu. His team is going to be called The Hawaii Tiger Sharks, and it will be another way to bring the islands of Hawai`i together as one to cheer for their own state team.

In an interview for *The Maui News*, a reporter asked, "Kaika, if there is one thing you can trace your success back to, what would it be?" Kaika replied, "There are actually three things to which I can attribute my success: First, my sixth grade teacher, Mr. Brodi Goshi, gave me a homework assignment to write out all the things I learned from all my wise entrepreneurial customers that summer when I made a decision to create my own business. Second, while in college, I read two very important books that changed the entire course of my future: *Creating Your Own Destiny* and *The Affluent Entrepreneur*. In reading these two books, I learned the truth in a quote from the works of this relatively unknown author:

"Think it, ink it!
Believe it, achieve it!"

Third, I studied the wisdom I learned from all my clients that I jotted down in a journal. I then applied all of their incredible advice from that summer onwards to my life in so many ways. Most importantly, it was J.C.'s suggestion that had the most profound impact on my life and ultimately gave me the perseverance to weather all the betrayal and storms that life would throw my way in the years to come. For this priceless wisdom, I am blessed and eternally grateful!"

EXERCISE:

Ink your desired future here. What are your five biggest goals you wish to achieve in your life?

1._____

2._____

3._____

4._____

5._____

ATTAINING THE VISION

Now that you have finished this book, what are you going to do? What actions are you going to take? What businesses are you going to start? Which kids are you going to mentor? What passions are you going to unleash?

Before you put down this book, I strongly encourage you to read the *50 Greatest Sales & Marketing Secrets for Entrepreneurs* and the many other included bonuses and special reports that follow and then apply these tools to your life and business. This is where the fun begins. It begins with action. You can read all the diet books in the world, but if you don't apply the wisdom in these books to your eating regimen, you will never lose weight. Another way to look at it is that knowledge is not power. Applied knowledge is power! Therefore, I am challenging you right now to apply the strategies, techniques, wisdom, inspiration, and stories from this book to your life and to do it right away.

My request to you is that before you continue on any further, I want you to stop reading this book and get out a pen or pencil, and in the ten exercise lines provided below, I want you to write out the top ten actions that you, your children, or grandchildren will commit to as a family moving forward that will set you up to create, grow, build, and / or nourish your business. Maybe it is reading another book, attending a seminar, investing in yourself by hiring a coach, finding a mentor, or purchasing fishing poles for your children.

EXERCISE:

Write ten actions that you commit to taking over the next 90 days:

1. _____
2. _____
3. _____
4. _____
5. _____
6. _____
7. _____
8. _____
9. _____
10. _____

Perhaps one of these ten action items is to go back through this book a second time and ensure that you write in all the exercises at the end of each chapter. Don't just read this book! Study this book, journal this book, and allow it to become your compass to chart your desired path to your ultimate destiny you desire to achieve.

Now that you have completed these ten items, ask yourself what you can do even better to help your son or daughter, grandson or granddaughter get started as an entrepreneur, or better yet find his or her passions. Also, what can you do to help your business grow better?

One of the things that drives me crazy is watching parents "push" their kids in a manner the kids don't want to be pushed. You have seen it before, where the Little League Dad does everything he can to promote his son because in his mind he believes that a scout from the New York Yankees will soon be drafting him. This behavior is absurd and it can really mess up a kid and permanently ruin a father-son or mother-daughter relationship. Just because it was your goal to play professional baseball doesn't mean you should push your goals off on to your kids.

Perhaps your older son or daughter was or is a stud athlete; that doesn't mean your younger ones will be. Let's face it; all kids are different, and they have different passions or skills. Your responsibility is not to create their lives for them.

Your responsibility as a parent or grandparent for your children or grandchildren is to do the following:

1. Encourage them to take 100 percent responsibility for their actions.
2. Identify any and all interests and talents they have (not what you have).
3. Expose them to opportunities in which they can develop those interests.
4. Drive them to the activities that hold their interest (coach them too).
5. Encourage them to stick it our throughout the season and not quit.
6. Always believe in them, and tell them how much you believe in them.
7. Nourish them in every way you can (emotionally).
8. Spend lots of time with them and become their best friend and role model.
9. Love them with all your heart and soul and communicate your love for them.
10. Step away, let them go do their passion, love them, and honor their choices.

(Oh, yeah...and don't forget to buy them fishing poles early in life and teach them how to fish for themselves in business and become entrepreneurs.)

If you can do these things, then you will have succeeded as a parent or grandparent, and you will enjoy watching the youth of today become our leaders of tomorrow.

In this book, you learned about never giving up, taking the leadership role in your life, learning to fish as an entrepreneur, believing in yourself, owning your visions, overcoming obstacles, counting the blessings in your life, and many other things. And the best is yet to come; don't forget to study, digest, and apply the *50 Greatest Sales & Marketing Secrets for Entrepreneurs*, plus the many other special reports, to your life. When you do these things, you will succeed as an entrepreneur and become the example for others in your family to follow.

Now that you have completed this book, please contact me to tell me what you liked and didn't like. What can I do to improve this book for the next edition? Most importantly, tell me where you are at in your journey, your business, and your life. Tell me how I can help you. Perhaps we can talk by phone, or better yet, maybe you can book me to travel to your location to speak for your organization.

I would like to offer you a no-obligation, complimentary 30-60 minute entrepreneurship consultation to help you better succeed in business, life, and parenting. My cell phone number is 206-310-1200 and my email address is Patrick@PatrickSnow.com. Due to spam, I would prefer that you text me instead of email me. Be sure to include your name and your time zone so we can coordinate your complimentary consultation via phone or Skype.

I hope you were encouraged by Kaika, Leilani, and this inspirational fable of free enterprise and self-leadership, and I hope you will apply these lessons to your life. I also hope you will follow the numerous special reports included at the end of this book.

I hope this book can be a beginning for us and not an ending. I hope that with this book in your hand, it can become the resource that you and your family need to succeed as a boy (or girl) entrepreneur in the game of free enterprise.

I hope you found what you were seeking in this book. I wish you all the success, prosperity, love, and happiness that life has to offer. I wish you the courage and strength to pursue your biggest passions in life. I wish you, your children, and grandchildren success with your entrepreneurial pursuits.

Now that you have learned how Kaika succeeded both in life and in small business, I challenge you to apply the story, lessons, mentors, and exercises from this book to your life and the life of your family. If you do, you too will succeed in business and life!

Dream, Plan, Execute, and Soar!

Mahalo and Aloha!

Your friend,

Patrick Snow

"Try not to become
a man of success,
but rather become
a man of value."

– Albert Einstein

OVERVIEW OF THE
GREATEST SECRETS

For as long as I can remember, I have always been an entrepreneur. This started in the St. Paul Grade School (in Owosso, MI) cafeteria during lunch hours when I started trading items in my sack lunch for other more desirable snacks. Then I realized money was more exciting than food, so at age twelve, I started as an entrepreneur as discussed earlier (just like Kaika). Today, in my late 40s, this means that I have been an entrepreneur for more than thirty-three years. During this time, I have made so many mistakes and learned from each one. I have experienced much failure and learned from it each time. In all, it totals about thirty-three years of "fishing" as an entrepreneur. In the beginning, I was a part-time fisherman, and now I am blessed to pursue entrepreneurship full-time.

As a professional speaker, I have been blessed to speak and travel all over the world. The question I get asked the most is, "Patrick, how did you do it? How did you quit your job, retire at thirty-six years old, and transition full-time into your business? How did you write a book? How did you become a professional speaker? How did you move to Maui and pursue the life of your dreams?" These are all great questions and the answers can be found in the next section of this book as I share with you the *50 Greatest Sales & Marketing Secrets for Entrepreneurs.* I have executed and implemented every single one of these suggestions, and I can assure you that they all work. They are completely responsible for how I took the leadership role in my life and pursued my dreams of achieving my own destiny based on "choice," not "chance"! You, too, can do the same, which is why I am including the next section in this book. I encourage you to study these 50 secrets and apply all the included special reports to both your life and business.

All of the items on this list of 50 are important, but the most important thing is this: BELIEVE IN YOURSELF! If you don't, no one else will. Without question, it is a belief in yourself, your dreams, your goals, and your visions that is the single greatest requirement to succeed as an entrepreneur. With this unshakable amount of belief and sheer determination, you must build yourself a platform upon which you can stand for the rest of your life to earn yourself not just a living, but a life! From this platform, you will be able to serve others, be an asset to your community, and change the world for the better.

For me, my platform was writing books: *Creating Your Own Destiny*, *The Affluent Entrepreneur*, *Becoming a Best-Selling Author*, and now *Boy Entrepreneur*. After failing 300 times to get paid as a professional speaker, as a Christian I had a "Come to Jesus Talk" to find out what I was doing wrong. The answer I got back, after studying the lives and stories of many of the same mentors whom Kaika came across the summer after sixth grade, was how true is the following quote from an unknown source:

"If you want what others have, you must do what others have done, and you will get what others have gotten!"

As a result, I spent five years of my life and $20,000 writing and publishing the first edition of *Creating Your Own Destiny*. This led me to 2,500 paid speaking engagements on three continents, more than 750 publishing coaching clients throughout the world, and a whole slew of media appearances on the radio and in print. As a result, I have stumbled across what I believe to be the world's greatest marketing secret in the history of all business. It is no surprise then that this secret is listed as number one on the list in the next section.

The "World's Greatest Marketing Secret in the History of All Business" is to write, publish, and promote your book as a better way to market your products or services as an entrepreneur. This strategy works if you are a boy or girl, man or woman, young or old. My youngest client is thirteen years old and my oldest is eighty-three. Hence, I have included an insert on book publishing in the back of the book as well.

If you would like to leverage this number one tool and harness its power of additional credentials, stronger credibility, and free publicity for your business, then text me on my private cell phone at 206-310-1200 with your name and time zone. I will then offer you a no-obligation, 30-60 minute, complimentary publishing consultation by phone or Skype (Skype ID is: "snow.patrick").

Don't worry if you are not the writing type; neither am I. I am a best-selling author, but certainly *not* a best-writing author. I have a team of editors, proofreaders, typesetters, and cover designers who can and will make you a star. If writing a book is not your thing, I understand! I would, however, recommend that you execute the other 49 items on this list if you want more out of life and want to experience the realization of your destiny!

(NOTE: After reading and applying these 50 Greatest Secrets to your life and business, I encourage you to read and study the other special reports I have included as well. I am extremely confident that you will benefit and be pleased with the ideas, strategies, and techniques shared in ALL of the enclosed special reports in the last section of this book.)

"Don't judge each day
by the harvest you reap,
but by the seeds you plant."

– Robert Louis Stevenson

50 GREATEST
SALES & MARKETING SECRETS
FOR ENTREPRENEURS

1. Write / Publish Book to Promote Your Business:
The "World's Greatest Marketing Secret" is to write, publish, and promote your book to attract more paying clients.

2. Invest in a Coach or a Mentor:
This strategy alone will save you thousands of dollars and many years of time. Learn from mentors' successes, and avoid their mistakes.

3. Join or Create a Mastermind Group:
Napoleon Hill defined a mastermind group as, "The coordination of knowledge and effort of two or more people, who work toward a definite purpose, in the spirit of harmony."

4. Include Your Family in Your Plan:
Succeeding in business takes time. Ask your family to be patient through the lean early years so all will benefit later in the prosperous years. It is important to get their support.

5. <u>Take Risks with Care and Preparation</u>:
Nothing worthwhile comes in life without risk. Study and analyze all risks to improve your chances of success.

6. <u>Keep Your Health as a Top Priority</u>:
Are you fit or fat? If you are fit, your business will flourish. The thinner your waistline, the thicker your bank account will become.

7. <u>Apply Four Wealth Creation Principles</u>:
A. Business Ownership B. Asset Leveraging C. Royalty or Residual Income D. Taking Advantage of Trends in the Marketplace.

8. <u>Surround Yourself with Other Successful People</u>:
You are the average of the five people you hang out with the most. Hang out with others who believe in your dreams, goals, and visions.

9. <u>Invest in Yourself with Books / Audio Programs</u>:
Read one inspirational book per week and listen to inspirational CDs while driving. Turn your car and your commute into your university.

10. <u>Break Your Rejection Gauge</u>:
Thicken your skin and remember: Some people will buy from you, some won't, so what NEXT? Someone else is waiting! (SW4)

11. <u>Outsource Whatever You Are Not Good At</u>: Hire people on contract (not as employees) to perform work in your business who have more skills, talents, and resources than you.

12. <u>Create Joint Venture Partnerships</u>: Don't hire and babysit a costly sales team (employees). Instead, partner with others and pay referral commissions when they bring paying clients to you.

13. <u>Pay All Your Teammates ASAP</u>: Once joint venture partners refer business, get them paid ASAP and they will further support you and refer more business.

14. <u>Leverage the Sixth Business Day of the Week</u>: Each weekend, go to bed early so you can awake and work Saturday and Sunday morning from 5 a.m. to 9 a.m. to catch up or get ahead.

15. <u>Eliminate "Time-Wasting" Activities</u>: Time is the most important asset you have, and more important than money. You can earn more money, but you can't earn more time.

16. <u>Study Successful and Famous Entrepreneurs</u>: The Biography Channel should be your favorite. Watch others' stories, read their books, apply their vision, and emulate their successes.

17. <u>Place Business Cards / Flyers on Bulletin Boards</u>: This may be the single greatest free marketing strategy on the planet. Place your marketing materials on all community bulletin boards you find.

18. <u>Make Compelling Offers to Your Prospects</u>: Once you uncover prospects' needs, make them an offer that solves their pain. Without your offer, they may never take action and buy.

19. <u>Give Large Discounts With Pre-Payment</u>: Collect your revenue up front in advance. The way to do this is to offer 5-10 percent pre-pay discounts when clients pay 100 percent upfront in advance.

20. <u>Accept Barter Offers</u>: Instead of losing a sale because prospects are cash flow poor, ask for and accept other assets they have in trade for your products or services. (When prospects can't pay by cash or credit.)

21. <u>Create a World-Class Brand Identity</u>: This includes your logo, website, books, letterhead, T-shirts, hats, bumper stickers, pens (anything you can use as giveaways).

22. <u>Apply the "3XT+3XM=30X ROI" Rule</u>: Successful businesses take three times longer than you want, cost you three times more than budgeted, but will net 30X return on investment.

23. <u>Use Sales Success Formula</u>:
Friends buy from friends, and people buy from whom they like. So develop: Trust + Respect + Need + <u>Asking</u> = $ale (T+R+N+A=$)

24. <u>Prospect Using the "50 Percent Rule"</u>:
The more business you close, the less time you have to find for more paying clients, so spend 50 percent of your working hours: Prospecting.

25. <u>Apply the "Rule of Seven"</u>:
Napoleon Hill says, "It takes seven bits of communication between buyer and seller in order for a sale to close." Don't stop prior to seven.

26. <u>The Fortune is Made in the Follow-Up</u>:
When everyone else gives up after 1-2 bits of communication, you "follow up" and close the sale with upwards of seven bits of communication.

27. <u>Walk-A-Mile in Your Prospect's Shoes</u>:
Everyone has "stuff" going on in his or her mind. So walk a mile in a prospect's shoes; empathize with his or her pain and he or she will do business with you.

28. <u>Focus on Marketing Instead of Advertising</u>:
Execute marketing strategies that are more effective (and often free), while advertising is more expensive and often does not work.

29. <u>Customize Your Services</u>:
Instead of providing a cookie cutter approach, un-cover needs of clients, and design products or ser-vices to fill their needs and solve their pain.

30. <u>Test & Measure, Trial & Error, Rinse & Repeat</u>:
Evaluate the sales and marketing strategies that have been successful in driving revenue, and execute the same techniques over and over again.

31. <u>Use Revenue War Board</u>:
Get a white war board for your office wall and list all prospects on it. Then use it for your sales road map for prospecting activities.

32. <u>Out Earn Your Bills</u>:
Instead of trying to save pennies here and there, know that the solution to your financial challenges are always solved when earning more money.

33. <u>Add More Value to the Marketplace</u>:
If you are not happy with your level of income, then you are to blame. This means you are not adding enough value to the marketplace.

34. <u>Leverage Technology to Serve More Clients</u>:
Doing conference calls (often) is just one more ex-ample of how to leverage your time and serve even more clients with the same number of hours.

35. <u>Do Workshops, Seminars, and Events</u>:
Speaking mentor Bob Moawad always said, "When I speak, business happens!" Speaking to a captive audience is your audition for more sales.

36. <u>Give Free Samples of Your Product or Service</u>:
Successful companies market new products by giving free samples to prospects. You too need to do the same.

37. <u>Focus on Your Business Vision</u>:
Don't worry about "how" you will make things happen. Focus on the vision and the "how" will slowly present itself over time.

38. <u>Create and View Your Vision Board Daily</u>:
Cut out and paste images of your dreams, goals, and visions onto a "vision board" and place this in your home office to look at daily.

39. <u>Connect with Prospects</u>:
Instead of selling prospects, serve them! Instead of marketing to prospects, connect with them. This is the secret to business success.

40. <u>Save Up a Cash Reserve in a Safe</u>:
Every time you get paid, take 10-25 percent off the top and place it in a safe hidden in your house until you get to $10K. Then use the rest for investing.

41. <u>Give of Your Time and Money</u>:
Share your time, gifts, and money with the youth of today so they can learn from you and become the leaders of tomorrow.

42. <u>Follow the Path to the Money</u>:
Ask for referrals from your existing clients. (They are your best salespeople.) Then pay them a referral commission.

43. <u>Post High Fees</u>:
Place your speaking, coaching, and consultation fees on your website; then be flexible, work within budget, and accept whatever client can afford.

44. <u>Be Bold with a "No Matter What" Mentality</u>:
Make a decision to become unstoppable in all areas of your business. It is not a matter of "if" but "when"!

45. <u>Solve Your Prospects' Pain</u>:
Find out where your prospects hurt and customize a product or service to cure their pain. Then under-promise and over-deliver!

46. <u>Going for the No's</u>:
Get 100 prospects to tell you "No." In doing so, you will earn big money and create a larger bank account. Want more sales? Make more sales presentations!

47. <u>Use "Flexible Planning" for Time Management</u>:
List all your "to do's" in one calendar. Next prioritize each item. Then follow the plan and whatever is left undone, move task to the next day.

48. <u>Leadership is NOT Given. It is Taken</u>:
Don't wait for another to lead you! Take the leadership role in all areas of your life (family, faith, wealth, and health).

49. <u>Determine Your Exit Strategy in Advance</u>:
Plan your life 5 to 20 years in advance so you can predetermine your destiny. Next take massive action to achieve massive results.

50. <u>Never Give Up (Ever!)</u>:
It's harder to quit and then start again than just to endure the journey. Believe in your visions, yourself, and your passions, and you will succeed!

"It is not the mountain we conquer,
but ourselves."

– Sir Edmund Hillary

15 START UP "MUST DOs" TO SUCCEED IN TRADITIONAL BUSINESS

1. You Must…Be so passionate about your product or service that you would promote it for free (because for a while this may be the case).

2. You Must…Be willing to risk everything in your life (with the exception of family and faith) for the success of your business.

3. You Must…Secure the "dot com" for the name of your business and trademark your brand so you can protect it from competitors.

4. You Must…Secure a good bookkeeper, accountant, and attorney to allow you to perform product creation, sales, and marketing for your business.

5. You Must…Keep your day job as long as possible so you can use it as seed money for your business. (You don't need to pay back day job income.)

6. You Must…Purchase your home and car prior to starting in business because without a guaranteed income, it is harder to secure these loans later.

7. You Must…Get emotional support from your spouse or partner to prepare for long hours and little pay in the beginning (in exchange for short hours and big pay in the end).

8. You Must…Know your target market intimately. Focus on this buyer all the way through the complete process from vision to creation.

9. You Must…Align yourself with others who are smarter, have more experience, more education, and a bigger network than you.

10. You Must…Retain 51 percent (or more) of the ownership and only sell 49 percent (and only if you need "Angel Investors" to get your company up and running.

11. You Must…Avoid having a business partner. Being married to someone at work almost never works. You retain control and make all final decisions as the CEO of your own business.

12. You Must...Work from home as long as you can (and have all teammates work virtually from home). This will save tens of thousands of dollars in office space.

13. You Must...Develop a strong Internet presence. This includes a website, branding, and search engine optimization.

14. You Must...Create a Unique Selling Proposition (USP) so you can distinguish yourself from your competition.

15. You Must...Be willing to sacrifice now as the janitor of your own business, so that later you benefit financially as the CEO and reap the results.

"Only put off for tomorrow
what you are willing
to die left undone."

– Pablo Picasso

50 HOME-BASED BUSINESS IDEAS FOR LESS THAN $1000

Artist
Author, Writer, Columnist, Blogger
Automobile Sales (Buy, Fix, Sell)
Bed and Breakfast
Business Services Consultant
Catering Company
College Recruiting Service
Computer Repair Consultant
Concierge Service
Crafts (in Your Area of Interest)
Daycare Placement Service
Editor
Educational Consultant to Schools
Exchange Student Coordinator
Executive Recruiter
Fence Building Business
Financial Advisor
Fish Tank Cleaning Service
Flower Delivery Service

Graphic Designer
Handyman Service (Carpentry)
Home Building Consultant
Home Inspection Service
Horticulture Service
Hospitality Service
House Cleaning Business
Insurance Representative
Interior Design Consultant
Janitorial or Carpet Cleaning
Landscape Design Business
Lawn Mowing Business
Manufacturers Representative
Massage Therapist
Motivational Speaker
Medical Transcriptionist
Musician for Hire
Network Marketing / Direct Sales
Nanny Placement Service
Pet Sitting / Pet Walking Business
Real Estate Appraiser
Real Estate Investor (Using Other People's Money)
Real Estate Agent
Scholarship Service
Selling Cookware

Success and Life Coach
Ticket Broker
Travel Agent
Vending Machine Business
Window Cleaning Service
Website Developer

"If I lost everything and
had to start over from scratch,
I would find a good network marketing
company and get to work."

– Donald Trump

20 REASONS WHY
NETWORK MARKETING
MAY BE YOUR BEST CHOICE

1. You will invest less than $500 in start-up costs.

2. You can build your business part-time (while still keeping your job).

3. You will eventually be able to break the dependence from your job.

4. You will not have a boss and can pick your own hours.

5. You can work from home, control your schedule, and have no commute.

6. You will have no overhead and no cost to bring products to market.

7. You won't have the challenges of manufacturing the product.

8. You will not have to deal with the legal challenges of structuring the business.

9. You can build your business regardless of education or work experience.

10. You can earn an unlimited amount of income with virtually no risk.

11. You get your own customized website from day one to market globally.

12. You can focus 100 percent of your time on the money-making part of your business.

13. You will be able to do the work one time, and get paid residually for life.

14. You get the opportunity to build a huge team without having to pay people.

15. You will get to travel all over the world to attend conferences.

16. You get a complete turnkey business with all training included.

17. You will have an opportunity to develop your leadership skills.

18. You get the opportunity to be personally mentored by successful leaders.

19. You will financially benefit off the hard work of others on your team.

20. You will attain financial freedom and develop lifelong friendships.

"The richest people in the world
look for and build
NETWORKS.
Everyone else looks for a
JOB."

– Robert Kiyosaki

30 WAYS TO BUILD WEALTH IN NETWORK MARKETING

1. Sponsor up, instead of down. Recruit those more talented than you.

2. Build your business seven days a week (even if you just do one thing a day).

3. Become a product of your product by using all services offered by your company.

4. Read one uplifting book per week. Readers are leaders.

5. Get all your new teammates paid within 30-60 days, whatever it takes.

6. Make sure your recruits and prospects get to meet company leaders.

7. Leverage your up-line sponsors via conference calls and team meetings.

8. Attend all company weeknight meetings and "Super Saturdays."

9. Pay a bonus to whoever brings the most people to meetings and conferences.

10. Share less details about your opportunity to more prospects.

11. Put more people's "butts in chairs" at meetings via carpooling.

12. Break your rejection gauge and overcome all your fears.

13. Place your business cards, flyers, and brochures on community bulletin boards.

14. Network with other MLM companies and target "unhappy distributors."

15. Practice the "Rule of Seven" when recruiting: keep in touch until they say, "No."

16. Use Ray Higdon's line: "It may or may not be for you; either way no big deal."

17. Never let someone else's opinion of you determine your reality.

18. Build and develop a foundation of 12 strong leaders.

19. Start your own conference call schedule. (Leadership is taken, not given.)

20. Subscribe to quote services where you get daily inspirational quotes by email.

21. Post an inspirational quote on social media sites (one per day).

22. Apply Sales Success Formula:
(Trust + Respect + Need + <u>Asking</u> = $)

23. "Some will, some won't, so what? NEXT. Someone else is waiting."

24. Put ten dimes in your pocket. Move all dimes to other pocket with each prospecting call.

25. Go for the No's and try and count to 100 rejections.

26. Don't appear to be pushy, desperate, or too eager. Just have fun.

27. Pick one company and make a commitment to stay with that company.

28. Use FORD (Family, Occupation, Recreation & Dreams) when prospecting.

29. If you are tired of starting over again and again, stop quitting.

30. Focus on your "Why" and the "How" will follow.

"It is not about closing sales,
it is about opening relationships."

– Kevin Knebl

SALES
SUCCESS FORMULA

Over the course of twenty years, I have interviewed thousands of employees from all walks of life (many in the sales and marketing fields). What do these people say they want? More time, more money, more freedom, more health, more love, and more happiness in life. Salespeople are no different. We all want these same things.

The good news is that salespeople are in a particularly good position to claim these things. Based on my research, I believe the best way to become wealthy in America is to own and operate your own business. The second best way is to be a salesperson. The sales profession is the only one without a limit to the amount of money you can earn! When you find that right sales position, all you need to do is to dream, plan, and execute, and your sales career will soar!

The key question, of course, is this: How can a salesperson get more out of life? I have an answer that's helped many people: By utilizing what I call the Sales Success Formula.

YOUR BIGGEST OBTACLE

Before we discuss the Sales Success Formula, it's important to understand that your biggest obstacle or competition isn't another company, and it's not another salesperson—it's your own mind. Your mind can either help you or hurt you depending on how you have programmed it to think. Rather than focusing on doubts, on reasons why you might not succeed, you must learn to believe and trust in yourself and in your unique passions.

The best way to learn how to believe and trust in yourself further is to set small, attainable goals and objectives for you to follow daily. As you execute your daily game plan and accomplish these objectives one by one, over time you will learn that you are capable of overcoming your obstacles and self-doubt. You will find yourself capable of achieving even more far-reaching goals. This is how to build internal trust and belief.

Once you have conquered self-doubt and won the mind battle, you will accomplish all in life that you can envision. Your mind will ignite a fire in your heart to execute your plan by taking actions in pursuit of your goals. As you experience this, you will become an unstoppable force of power fully capable of achieving more success and freedom than you could have ever imagined. You will literally rise to the top of your organization and become the person you've always wanted to become.

THE FORMULA

Now that you understand the power of your mind, it's important to analyze why people purchase goods or services from one organization but not others. If you ask buyers why they awarded a contract to one company and not another, you quickly will learn the key: relationships. People buy from people they like. Friends buy from friends. It is that simple. If you want to make more sales, develop more solid relationships. The salesperson who is best at developing relationships will ultimately produce the biggest results, period.

To develop more solid relationships, I suggest you use what I call the Sales Success Formula. The success formula is:

Trust (T) + Respect (R) + Need (N) + Ask (A)=Money ($)

Like every formula, each part must occur to reach the ultimate goal, in this case, sales. Trust is absolutely crucial to close sales. Your prospect may respect your company, and he also may have a need, but if he doesn't trust you as a person, he will never buy from you.

To build trust, you must show the buyer that you care about his success. When a buyer learns how much you care about him and his organization's success, then he will trust you. The best way to earn this trust and respect is to make sure you let the buyer speak 90 percent of the time, and you only speak 10 percent of the time.

Another way to build trust in the relationship is to ask about the buyer and his or her interests, outside activities, etc. Questions can include ones about his commute, his working conditions, his family and children, and his hobbies—these and others will give you a better idea of the buyer and his or her interests.

Respect is another key component to this equation. It's possible to trust someone but not respect him for whatever reason. The best way to build respect is to follow up on action items as promised by responding in a timely manner. Also, make certain that you show up on time for all appointments or call if you are going to be late. Finally, always make the prospect know that you value his business.

It is extremely important to qualify need as quickly as you can in the sales cycle because without need (regardless of how much trust and respect you have established), you will never be able to close the sale. To discover a prospect's need, ask him whether he is in the market for your product or service. If he won't tell you, find others within the organization to see whether they can advise you of the organization's need.

All too often, salespeople forget to ask whether there is a need, as well as to ask for the prospect's business. A buyer could have all the trust and respect in the world for you and your organization, but if he doesn't have the need, he will never buy! If this is the case, move to the next prospect and then qualify his need prior to building the relationship.

THE RESULTS

To become the top salesperson in your organization, utilize this success formula to develop solid relationships based on trust, respect, need, and asking for business. To make this happen, execute your game plan daily and don't take rejection personally (the word "next" is the most powerful word in this field). If you implement and follow this formula (T+R+N+$\underline{A}$=$), you will become unstoppable and earn more money than you could have ever imagined. This increased income will ultimately help you get more out of life!

"The written page
is the only way
the dead can
teach the unborn."

– Abraham Lincoln

WORLD'S GREATEST MARKETING SECRET

Let's face it; in recent years, everything you learned to build your business successfully has changed and may no longer be effective! You were first taught to spend money on advertising. Next, to leverage the Internet by using social media. Neither of these strategies may be achieving your desired results. The problem is consumers no longer believe in advertising, and the Web is more competitive than ever. As a small-business consultant, I am frequently asked for a better way to attract more paying clients.

My answer is simple: Write and publish your book, give it away to your prospects, and attract more paying clients! This flat out works! It will allow you to stand out from the crowd, boost your credentials, and give you even more credibility. To succeed in applying this marketing secret to your business, you will want to create a bestseller.

FIVE REQUIREMENTS FOR BECOMING A BEST-SELLING AUTHOR:

1. <u>Execute a Book Marketing Campaign for Life</u>: A successful book is 5 percent writing and 95 percent promotion. Book marketing is often compared to raising a child. As parents, we spend nine months bringing a child into this world, then 18-22 years raising that child. We must do the same with book marketing and spend 20 years or more promoting a book. Many fail in this area as they only market their books for 90 days and then they give up.

2. <u>Design a World-Class Book Cover</u>: The best way to get your prospect's attention is with the cover design of your book. We are taught as young children never to judge a person by the way he looks, but rather by his character. However, this is not true with book covers. The first impression of your cover design is almost exclusively how most people will judge the content of your book; hence, the reason for having a world-class cover design.

3. <u>Use a Compelling Title</u>: Often your book title will appear in print without its cover, so your title must intrigue readers. There are three award-winning title formulas. Therefore, if you don't know these formulas, it is not a good idea to select your own title. In a perfect world, your title needs to communicate to the reader exactly what the book's content is about, and this can be tricky. Therefore, leave title

creation up to the experts, but do make sure you own the domain name of your book title as well.

4. <u>Create an Amazing Introduction</u>: The average person only reads through the first 20 pages of a book, so your Introduction must compel people to keep reading throughout. Most authors write non-fiction introductions about themselves and why they wrote this book. This is a big mistake! You need to write the introduction about the reader and show how your book can solve his or her pain. When you do this, your reader will be compelled to read the entire book.

5. <u>Have Good Content</u>: If you are writing fiction, your book needs to be full of tales of love and death. If non-fiction, your book needs to be jam-packed full of stories, case studies, and real-life examples, which feature your offerings. Your readers do not want to be taught anything; they want to be inspired to learn of real-life people stepping into their destinies. Therefore, include lots of stories in your book and it will be successful.

Using this strategy and applying these five requirements, I guarantee that you will attract more paying clients to your doorstep.

"Only those who will risk
going too far
can possibly find out
how far one can go."

– T.S. Eliot

SIX STEPS
TO FLUSH YOUR JOB

(& COME OUT SMELLING LIKE A ROSE)

1. <u>Overcome Your Fears</u>:

    Fear stands for: Falsely Expecting Awful Results
    or False Evidence Appearing Real. Do what you
    fear, and the fear will disappear! Don't focus on
    what may happen to you (I won't be able to pay
    my bills or I'll fail at this venture), but focus on
    what you can control. Overcoming your fears will
    set you free to create your own destiny!

2. <u>Take Action and Start Your Own Business</u>:

    You are unhappy at work! Admit it, and make a
    decision to do something about it. The days of
    job security are long gone, so NOW is the time
    to take charge of your future and start your own
    business. You are the only one who can make the
    decision to do what makes you happy.

3. <u>Pursue Your Most Marketable Passion</u>:

   Become your own boss! Do what you love and the money will follow! What is your most marketable passion? Brainstorm all the ways you can start a business doing what you love and what the marketplace needs most.

4. <u>Customize Your Business</u>:

   Put yourself in your customer's shoes. How do you want to be treated? What is good customer service to you? Ask your prospects exactly what it is that they want and need; then create a customized solution to meet their needs. This is how you build a successful business.

5. <u>Build Your Business Daily</u>:

   Prospect 50 percent of your working hours. As a result of developing this work ethic, you will have an endless flow of incoming clients driving revenue to your business. Leverage the early morning weekend hours either to catch up or get ahead in your business.

6. <u>Break Free from Dependence on Your Job</u>:

Make your dream happen! Keep your job until you have one year's income saved and are debt free. Alternatively, find a job that allows you time to work on building your business. If you want freedom, you will find a way to make it happen. Once you are in this position, leave your job in pursuit of your business and never look back!

(DISCLAIMER: A job is a good thing. It provides you a means to take care of your family, pay your bills, buy groceries, etc. But sooner or later, all jobs come to an end (layoffs, mergers, acquisitions, downsizing). The big question becomes, "When do I quit my job to focus full-time on my business?" My answer is, "You want to keep your day job as long as you can." Why? Because your "day job income" is the best 'seed money' you can access to grow your business. You do not have to pay back this investment since it is yours and you earned it. Keep your job until you are debt free, your business income surpasses your day job income, and you have one year's worth of income in the bank. Then you have my blessing to flush your job and join the ranks of full-time entrepreneurs.)

"I will do today
what others don't,
so I will have tomorrow
what others won't."

– John Addison

ABOUT THE AUTHOR

PATRICK SNOW is an international best-selling author, professional keynote speaker, publishing, speaking, and book-marketing coach. He first discovered his gift for speaking at the age of seventeen while giving the pre-game speeches to his high school football team. Since then, Patrick has electrified more than 2,500 audiences on three continents to create their individual and organizational destinies.

As a publishing coach, Patrick has mentored more than 750 clients throughout the world to publish successfully their fiction, non-fiction, memoir, legacy, or children's book.

Patrick's "DESTINY" message has been recognized on TV, in magazines, and in major newspapers such as *The New York Times*. His book and family photo was also featured as a cover story in the December 5th, 2002, issue of *USA TODAY*. He has also been featured in a Spanish edition of *Forbes*.

Patrick is author of the international bestseller, *Creating Your Own Destiny*, which has sold more than

250,000 copies in five languages and 108 countries worldwide since its first printing in 2001. As a result, this book and his second book, *The Affluent Entrepreneur*, have both been purchased by John Wiley & Sons in New York and have been republished under the Wiley imprint.

On Patrick's newest book, *Boy Entrepreneur*, he returned to his passion of self-publishing. He is also a contributing author to numerous other books, including *Chicken Soup for the Soul: Life Lessons for Mastering the Law of Attraction.*

Originally from Michigan, Patrick graduated from the University of Montana in 1991. He lived in the Seattle area for more than twenty years until April 2013, when he and his fiancée, Nicole, moved to Maui, Hawai`i.

ABOUT BEST-SELLER PUBLISHING COACHING

If you want to stand out from your competition, strengthen your credentials, and get free publicity, then writing and publishing a book is your best option! Your book will become a lead-generating tool that helps boost your profits by securing highly-paid speaking engagements and attracting more coaching and consulting clients.

Don't feel overwhelmed by the thought of writing a book. Let international best-selling author, professional speaker, and publishing and book marketing coach Patrick Snow guide you through the process with one-on-one and group coaching calls, unlimited email and text access, an easy-to-follow publishing coaching road map, a 52-step book marketing business plan, and his life-changing Best Seller Publishing Institute.

Patrick Snow has sold more than 250,000 copies of his books in five languages and 108 countries. He has also mentored more than 750 clients to publish their own books successfully (fiction or non-fiction). Patrick Snow will simplify the process, saving you both time and money, serve as your coach for life, and guide you through all the steps in the publishing process, and in book marketing, media, publicity, speaking, coaching, and consulting.

For more information, visit one of his websites listed below and then text him with your name, time zone, and the best time to redeem a 30-60 minute, no obligation publishing consultation by phone or Skype.

www.ThePublishingDoctor.com
www.BestSellerBookCoaching.com
www.PatrickSnow.com
Mobile: 206-310-1200

ABOUT DESTINY ACHIEVER'S CLUB

Patrick Snow offers a private, by "invitation only" membership for his readers and audience who want to take charge of their lives, become the captains of their own ships, and the creators of their destinies. If this is something you are interested in, you can review member benefits below:

1. eBook / PDF of international best-seller, *Creating Your Own Destiny*

2. eBook / PDF of *The Affluent Entrepreneur*

3. eBook / PDF of *Boy Entrepreneur*

4. Permission to forward all these eBooks by email to up to <u>One Million Friends & Family</u>

5. Patrick Snow's: 50 Greatest Sales & Marketing Secrets for Entrepreneurs (plus all of his other special reports)

6. Patrick Snow Weekly Conference Call Every Monday

7. Lifetime Membership with <u>no expiration date</u>, ever! This is not a joke! That is 52 calls a year and 520 calls over ten years.

Normal membership fee is $1,495, but if you join within one week of completing this book, you can access your membership and have access to Patrick Snow's weekly calls for $795. To join, simply text Patrick Snow your email address and he will reply with paperwork for you to become a member.

www.DestinyAchieversClub.com
www.PatrickSnow.com
Mobile: 206-310-1200

BOOK PATRICK SNOW
TO SPEAK AT YOUR
NEXT EVENT

When it comes to choosing a professional speaker for your next event, you will find no one more respected or successful—no one who will leave your audience or colleagues with a more renewed passion for life—than Patrick Snow, one of the most gifted speakers of our generation. Since 1986, Patrick Snow has delivered more than 2,500 inspirational presentations worldwide.

Whether your audience is 10 or 10,000, in North America or abroad, Patrick Snow can deliver a customized message of inspiration for your meeting or conference. Patrick understands your audience does not want to be "taught" anything, but is rather interested in hearing stories of inspiration, achievement, and real-life people stepping into their destinies.

As a result, Patrick Snow's speaking philosophy is to humor, entertain, and inspire your audience with passion and stories proven to help people achieve extraordinary results. If you are looking for